Understanding Algebra

How to Master Basic Algebra and Pass Exams

Dr Graham Lawler

Understanding Algebra

How to Master Basic Algebra and Pass Exams

Dr Graham Lawler

The author's rights have been asserted.

978-1-84285-385-6

Produced and Published by Studymates

Studymates
New Lamorna House
Abergele
LL22 7DY

Studymates is a division of GLMP Ltd
and is not affiliated, endorsed or sponsored by any external organisation.

For Alex, who is now old enough to understand.

Understanding Algebra
How to Master Basic Algebra and Pass Exams

Better English (2nd ed)
Better French (3rd ed)
Better French 2
Better German
Better Spanish
British History
Business Communication
Calculus
Chemistry: As Chemistry Explained
Chemistry: Chemistry Calculations Explained (3rd ed)
European History
Genetics (3rd ed)
Growing Workplace Champions
Hitler and Nazi Germany (3rd ed)
Lenin, Stalin and Communist Russia (2nd ed)
Organic Chemistry (2nd ed)
Perfect Grammar
Plant Physiology
Practical Drama (2nd ed)
Project Management (2nd ed)
Shakespeare
Social Anthropology (2nd ed)
The Academic Essay (3rd ed)
The English Reformation
The Theatre Makers (2nd ed)
Trigonometry
Understanding Literature and Film
Understanding Maths (5th ed)
Understanding Poetry (2nd ed)
Understanding the Numbers
Warfare 1792-1918
Your Master's Thesis
Your Ph.D Thesis

Many more titles in development

Block of flats image courtesy of The hornet at English Wikipedia

Contents

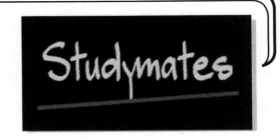

1 What is the Point of Algebra?

One-Minute Overview

The purpose of algebra is a mystery to many students and parents. The fact is that it is seen as irrelevant, as a useless mind numbing exercise and as something that 'egg heads' work through, just for the sake of it. Nothing could be further from the truth.

In this chapter, we will look at:
*   Why algebra was invented;
*   Who invented algebra;
*   Where do we use algebra in real life;
*   How to think algebraically.

Life in the Twenty-First Century

There are some things in life that we can be fairly comfortable with predicting. One of these is that life in the twenty-first century is going to be one of rapid change. Research has shown that the adult of the future will have to be able to respond quickly to changing circumstances. There is no such thing as a job for life.

Older people may remember a time in the last century when young people could expect to join an organisation and stay there for the whole of their career.

These days we are more likely to have a situation where people have two or three careers in their lifetime. Think about it, a child going to school in 2020 could still be working in 2070.

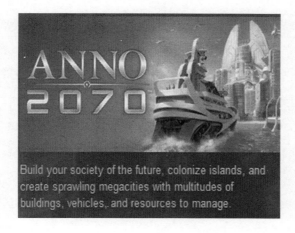

Build your society of the future, colonize islands, and create sprawling megacities with multitudes of buildings, vehicles, and resources to manage.

take a look at steampowered.com, on the day we checked you could create your own 2070

The truth is we have no idea what 2070 will be like. There will be jobs that have not yet been invented. There will be machines that we can only imagine.
There are already robots that can help elderly, infirm people into and out of bed.
So we cannot teach that child everything they need to know in their lives but we can be absolutely sure of one thing. They will have problems that they will need to be able to solve.
To be successful, the citizens of the future will need to have a good basic education but also need to be able to think analytically.
They need to be able to:
*   solve problems,
*   write solutions to problems in a general form,
*   communicate their ideas to other people.

So why is algebra important?

Algebra develops your thinking ability. It also gives you quite sophisticated thinking tools that you can use in industry – and despite what is popularly thought, the algebra you learn in class is more important than ever before.

Can you think of just one common use for algebra?

Most businesses use spreadsheets in some way or other – spreadsheet formulae are just algebraic statements that do the calculations for you, but if the formulae are wrong, you get the wrong answer.

So there is an even greater need to understand algebra than ever before. You really do ignore it at your peril. Algebra can literally help your career progression. The spreadsheet shown here is a very simple one for a simple set of calculations. The second picture shows the spreadsheet with the formulae on show – look at all the algebra in column D.

	A	B	C	D	E
1	item	quantity	price	Total	
2	Buns	3	£1.50	£4.50	
3	cakes	3	1.75	£5.25	
4	toffee	2	0.99	£1.98	
5	sticky fudge	1	0.5	£0.50	
6				£12.23	
7					

	A	B	C	D
1	item	quantity	price	Total
2	Buns	3	1.5	=(B2*C2)
3	cakes	3	1.75	=(B3*C3)
4	toffee	2	0.99	=(B4*C4)
5	sticky fudge	1	0.5	=(B5*C5)
6				=SUM(D2:D5)
7				

Screenshots reprinted by permission of the Microsoft Corporation

These are very simple formulae but it does give you an example of what is involved.

So why do we need algebra?

The simple answer is that algebra gives us general rules. Look at this example to see what we mean.

Start	1	2	3	4
End	5	7	9	11

What is done to the start number to get the end number? In each case we manipulate the start number with two operations.

The first is to multiply by 2 and the second is to add 3.

So in each case, we have

start number × 2 + 3 = end number.

This is a general rule that frees up our thinking. Now we can work out the end number for any start value. Say we start with 10 – multiply this by 2, then add 3, and the end number should be 23.

We could say

$$2s + 3 = e$$

This is a very basic example of how algebra works. The point we want you to understand is that by using algebra, you can understand patterns and sequences that occur in real life.

Why is this important ?

When you understand these patterns and sequences, you can make predictions about what is going to happen in the future. This is often referred to as 'mathmagic'. In fact it is not magic at all – it is the skill of understanding patterns and thereby being able to predict what will happen.

This is what gives us real power. It is this ability to make these predictions that is the most exciting aspect of algebra, this is what fires most mathematicians.

The purpose of this book is to make sure you have some basic skills that will support your learning. But there is one caveat with which you must agree.

There is only one way to learn mathematics, and that is to do mathematics.

You do need to sit down and have a go at the problems that are in this book.
You need to grapple with the contexts and, as you do, you will join all those who have ever learned mathematics. It is an essential part of the journey to make errors and to learn from them.

So where did algebra come from?
Algebra is a word that is derived from an early Arabic mathematician called Al-Khwarizimi. He most certainly was a genius of his time. We actually know very little about his life but we do know that his family came from Khorezm, at that time in Persia. He worked in the House of Wisdom in Baghdad in present day Iraq. This was a centre for scientific research and teaching. It was his book on algebra that both gave name to the area of study and moved the subject forward. He stated at the time that he wanted to support scholars in the solution of complex problems that occurred at that time. This is still the case today. Algebra allows us to see general patterns and to use this knowledge to solve problems. Al-Khwarizimi went further than this – he wanted to understand and develop the more theoretical aspects of algebra, the science of equations.
By determining rules, we can follow them and calculate answers to matters that previously we could not solve.

For example, you often see calculations like this in early mathematics textbooks.
The diagram shows a playground that measures 10 m by 5 m.
Find the area of the playground.

We can use a simple piece of algebra to show the relationship between length and area.

$$\text{area} = \text{width} \times \text{height}$$

$$A = w \times h$$
$$= 10 \times 5$$
$$= 50 \text{ m}^2.$$

A simple example but one which shows an important principle and hints at the power of equations.

That is the point; by studying algebra, you are improving your ability to think. That makes you a superior person, it puts you into the top fifth of the population

'Thinking is the hardest work there is,
which is probably the reason why so few engage in it.'
Henry Ford

Fear and algebra
Many students develop a fear of algebra because they find it hard.

If you do get stuck, think about what you would do if you were dealing with numbers instead of letters.

Algebra is based on the same set of rules, so you can use the same methods to solve problems. It will help you to understand the work. This is called specialising.

However, in this chapter we want to concentrate on getting you ready to learn. That means examining your own motivations and challenging your own perceptions. In other words, it means a taking long hard think about yourself. What is it that you cope well with and what is it that frightens you? Think about this for a moment.

Personal Journal
We suggest that you consider writing a 'personal journal' to record your thoughts and fears – this is a great way of challenging them and taking control of your life, rather than letting events control you.

Keep the journal private – it is for you, not for anyone else. It is your private world where you can channel your thoughts and develop the confidence that you deserve.

Feeling the fear
Fear comes from within. It is how you respond to events that affect you, rather than the events themselves.

Think about this for a moment. Everyone has downsides in life, so why is it that some people give up and others move on with a smile on their face?

Quite simply it is because they can control how they respond. They are in charge of their emotions.

When it comes to mathematics, many people take fright. Certainly in the western world people brag, 'I am no good at maths'. Yet they wouldn't dream of admitting that they cannot read.

This attitude will keep you back in the twenty-first century.

Parents, and sometimes teachers, will say 'Well I could never do maths when I was your age'.

This is the wrong thing to say to a child. The adult is telling the child that it is possible to live in today's society without this level of knowledge, yet how many would say this to a child about their spelling?

Yes it is meant in sympathy but actually it is sending the wrong message. Children need to be able to spell and they need to be numerate. In the same way, adults need to be numerate and to be able to use algebra. Most people do not take fright when they see sentences in, say, French or German and yet become panic stricken when they see a few symbols of algebra on a page. Algebra is a language in the same way that French or German are languages.

Mathematics is the Language of the Universe

In her excellent book *Feel the Fear and Do It Anyway* (Rider, 1997), Susan Jeffers gives good advice on overcoming feelings of insecurity. She writes about that nagging little voice inside all our heads that she calls 'the chatterbox', which is in fact the voice of our lower self.

How to silence the internal chatterbox
The way to silence that chatterbox is by affirmations.

What is an affirmation?
An affirmation is a positive statement that you can say to yourself. This has the effect of lifting you mentally. Think of your brain as a muscle. In the same way that you have to exercise your body, you also need to exercise your brain – affirmations are a great way of doing this.

Just pause for a moment, sit back and …

b—r—e—a—t—h—e

Now make an affirmation. One of the people in our office said that her affirmation is

'I am loved and I am loving. I am strong and I am powerful.'

Who could fail to be inspired with words like these? I hope you find them as uplifting as we do. See how powerful you become by simply affirming your belief.

The other side of this coin is to label yourself as a failure. We saw a young man in Taunton literally labelling himself negatively. He was walking through the town wearing a shirt with the word 'loser' printed across the front, for all of the world to see. You become what you believe. Believe you are powerful and successful and then you will become powerful and successful. If you believe you are a failure then don't be surprised if that is what you become.

Changing your physiology

Think about how you sit or stand or walk. Your body needs oxygen to work effectively but if your chest cavity is depressed you simply cannot get the oxygen into your lungs – so how can you expect your body and your brain to work well?

In the same way, for peak performance you need to consider your diet. To become a champion in any field you need to provide your body and brain with the right food. Over a third of Americans are obese. That means more than 30% of their body mass is made up of fat.

Here in the UK we are not far behind. Thomas Mofat , a seventeenth century American medic said, '

We are digging our graves with our teeth'.

How true this is today. To change the way you feel – to be empowered, to feel great – you need the right exercise and the right food.

What about shortcuts?

There are some shortcuts to improving how you feel. One is to stand up straight and let the tensions in you simply 'wash away'. Changing your physiology changes the way you breathe and this can help you to feel better.

So, why are you reading all of this in a book on algebra?

Quite simply, you cannot perform well mentally if you cannot perform well physically. Doing algebra, and indeed mathematics, is like being a mental tradesman. In the same way that a plumber will select the right tool for the right job from a toolbox, so a mathematician needs to make the same decisions concerning mathematics tools.

In the same way that a plumber may use a wrench, so a mathematician may choose to use a mental tool to solve a problem – but not if they are mentally and physically unfit.

Why do we need algebra?

We have already asked this question, and to some extent answered it, but here we want to take you into this a little deeper.

Robert Reich was a member of President Clinton's US administration and wrote a very influential book called *The Work of Nations*.
In this he explains how society has changed since the middle to late 1970s.

Different types of jobs

Reich explains how workers can be put into one of three groups – in-person providers, routine producers and symbolic analysts.
In-person providers are people who do jobs that cannot currently be done by machines. For example the office cleaner or the person in the fast-food outlet who serves you fries are in-person providers. Similarly teachers are in this group. Routine producers are people who work in routine semi-skilled jobs. These jobs, like making

washing machines in factories, have largely been re-placed by robots or exported to lower cost economies.

Professor Robert Reich

People in both of these groups have seen a fall in their incomes in real terms.

The final group are called symbolic analysts. Symbolic analysts are people who use symbols, manipulate them and solve problems symbolically in a way that can then be applied back to the real world to solve problems.

Symbolic analysts are not the same as graduates.

You can be a symbolic analyst if you solve problems at any level in industry. Think of this as a 'troubleshooter' type of job. This is exactly the type of job in which there is a shortage of qualified men and women – and this is where algebra comes into its own and where algebra and this book can help give you a major advantage.

A good example, of a symbolic analyst, is the person who works out the minimum distance route for a delivery van.

Algebra helps you to learn how to think systematically.

It enables you to deal with changes in a system and to define rules that are both simple and elegant.

The Elegant Equation?
Can an equation really be elegant? Well, yes it can.
Look at Einstein's work on relativity. He summarised his work with the elegant and beautiful equation

$$E = mc^2$$

Here Einstein tells us that

energy = mass × the speed of light squared

Think about the beauty of this equation – Einstein found that a law of the Universe could be described in such a straightforward manner. This is the power of algebra.

Thinking algebraically

There is a style of thinking that mathematicians call algebraic or mathematical thinking. This style, or approach, to thinking is an important life skill.

Many people say that they never use algebra after they leave school. Whilst this is undoubtedly true in terms of manipulating symbols, it is unlikely that they have never used mathematical thinking.

Here is a simple example. Imagine putting up shelves in your home. Say you need 4 screws for each shelf, what will the total number of screws needed? Think about this for a moment.

The number of screws will be 4 times the number of shelves.

This is a simple example of a generalisation.

Are there other areas in life that use algebra?

There most certainly are – particularly in business. There are established rules, written as equations, that can be applied to solve problems.

There are equations that calculate how fast something is travelling.
There are equations that calculate the minimum pathway through a production process – this makes it possible to calculate the shortest route through a production process, thereby getting the raw materials into the final form in the shortest possible time. This saves time, and therefore money, and gets the product to market as soon as possible.

Tutorial
Progress Questions

Using your journal, answer these questions.

- What controls you? Are you really controlled by symbols on a page?
- What would it mean to you if you could improve your education?
- Would this lead to better job prospects?

Discussion Points
'Algebra has had a bad press – people have memories from their school days that still affect their judgement.'

Discuss this with another person. Is it true for you? And the other person? Make an entry in your journal

Practical Assignment
As stated previously, your journal is a personal document for charting your development. We therefore recommend that you keep it private.

In your journal write down a vision for yourself.

- Where will you in three years time?
- What type of job will you be doing?
- Will you be living somewhere else?

Go on, dare to dream and enjoy!

Study Tips
Learn to 'mind map'. Mind mapping was invented by Tony Buzan and it is an extraordinary way of learning and recording information. Read Tony's book The Mind Map Book (BBC books).

References
The Work of Nations R Reich 978-0679736158

2 Number Patterns and Sequences

One-Minute Overview

Algebra is all about patterns and sequences – it is about looking for the general from the particular.

In this chapter, you will learn how to:
- Describe square numbers, cube numbers and triangle numbers;
- Describe a sequence;
- Make simple generalisations.

Square Numbers

Some numbers make a pattern that can be shown as a geometric pattern.
Look at this sequence.

Can you see the pattern? Look at what you can see – what have the patterns got in common?

Don't worry if you can't see the connection yet – frankly, most people will not.
This is an important part of learning mathematics.

The next number is 16. Here it is:

Can you see the pattern yet? Look at the length and width of the rectangles, what do you notice? Can you predict the next number?

The next number in the sequence is 25 – but why? Look at the arrangement of the dots. You should see that the pattern of the dots is a square, so these numbers are called square numbers.

Look again at the squares.

1 is a square number because it is 1 × 1
4   is 2 × 2
9   is 3 × 3
16 is 4 × 4
25 is 5 × 5

and so on

Now you can see what these numbers have in common. They follow the pattern that they have the same number of dots in the rows as they have in the columns (well they are squares, so that is what you would expect).

Can you predict what the next number will be? This is the true power of the mathematics, the ability to predict and to be right.

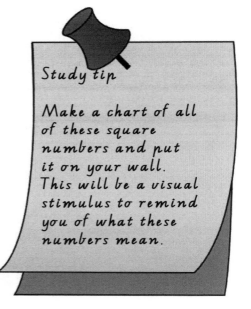

Study tip

Make a chart of all of these square numbers and put it on your wall. This will be a visual stimulus to remind you of what these numbers mean.

It will be useful to know and be able to recall all the square numbers at least up to 15 × 15.

As well as this you need to know and be able to recall 20 × 20
and
25 × 25

The sequence with this formula

$$n^{th} \text{ term} = n^2$$

is the sequence of square numbers. The first four terms are 1, 4, 9 and 16. The 10th term is 100 (10 × 10) and the 20th term is 400 (20 × 20).

Look again at the sequence 1, 4, 9, 16. None of the rules 'add 3', 'add 5' or 'add 7' work here because the number to add on changes. The rule is first add 3, then add 5, then add 7. So we need to add 9 to get the next term

16 + 9 = 25.

You can see this is correct because we know the next term is 5 × 5.

Square Roots

What exactly is the square root of a number?

The easiest way to think of this is to consider the square numbers we talked about when we were explaining square numbers. Remember the square number 9 was generated by 3 × 3. So 3 is the square root of 9, because 3 × 3 = 9. In the same way, 5 is the square root of 25 because 5 × 5 = 25. And 10 is the square root of 100 for the same reason.

The Square Root Symbol

$\sqrt{}$ is the symbol for the square root of a number. So the square root of 9 is written as $\sqrt{9}$ and mathematically we write $\sqrt{9} = 3$

Exercise 2.1

Write down the square roots of all the square numbers up to 225.

Cube Numbers

      1 cm cube   2 cm cube   3 cm cube

To work out the volume multiply the length by the width by the height.

Look at the 1 cm cube.

$$V = l \times w \times h$$
$$= 1 \times 1 \times 1$$
$$= 1 \text{ cm}^3.$$

So the first cube number is 1.

Now do the same with the 2 cm cube.

$$V = 2 \times 2 \times 2$$
$$= 8 \text{ cm}^3.$$

This means the second cube number in the sequence is 8.

Don't confuse 2^3 with 2 × 3.
2^3 means
2 × 2 × 2
2 × 2 = 4
then
4 × 2 = 8

Now do the same with the third cube, the one with all sides 3 cm long.

$$V = 3 \times 3 \times 3$$
$$= 27 \text{ cm}^3.$$

Now we do the same with the next number in the sequence.

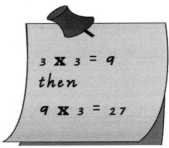

3 **X** 3 = 9
then
9 **X** 3 = 27

Here we have not drawn a cube, but if it makes things easier then draw your own cube and calculate the fourth cube number. Here is the calculation.

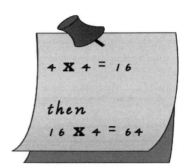

4 **X** 4 = 16
then
16 **X** 4 = 64

$$V = 4 \times 4 \times 4$$
$$= 64 \text{ cm}^3.$$

So this means that the first four cube numbers are 1, 8, 27 and 64.

What are the next three cube numbers? Have a go at this now.

Look at this formula, n^3. Put 1 into the formula – what do you get?

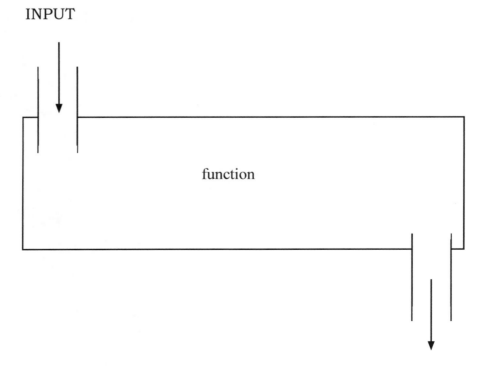

INPUT

function

Output

You should have found that you get 1. Let's look at this more closely using the idea of function machines.

Here if we put 1 into the function machine, we operate n^3 on it.

But what does 'operating n^3' mean?

$$n^3 \text{ means } n \times n \times n$$

So when we enter 1 into this function machine it operates as $1 \times 1 \times 1$ so we get 1 out. What would we get if we put 2 into this function machine? ... don't worry we'll wait.

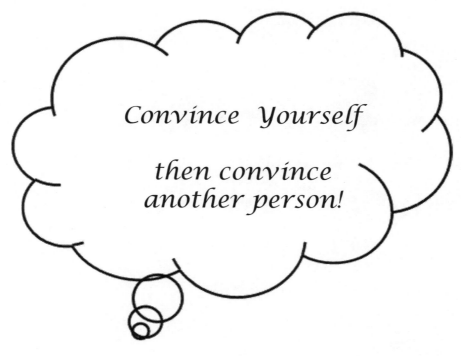

Convince Yourself

then convince another person!

You should have found you get 8 out.

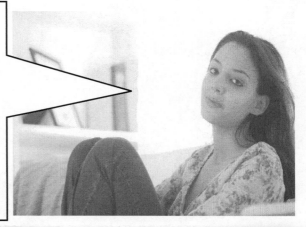

Think about it – if we put 2 into the function machine we are operating

$2 \times 2 \times 2$.

So $2 \times 2 = 4$, then $4 \times 2 = 8$.

So the first two numbers in this sequence are 1 and 8.
These are the first two numbers in the sequence of cube numbers.

Exercise 2.2

Write down the first five cube numbers. We have the first two, namely 1 and 8. Remember the pattern

$$1 \times 1 \times 1 = 1$$
$$2 \times 2 \times 2 = 8.$$

So what are the next three?

Triangular numbers

1   3   6

What are the next three numbers in the sequence?

Look at the pattern again. It starts with 1, then it is 1 + 2, then 1 + 2 + 3, then 1 + 2 + 3 + 4. The next number will be the answer to 1 + 2 + 3 + 4 + 5, which is ...?

Work out the rest of the sequence for the first ten triangular numbers.

    Understanding Algebra

What is a Sequence ?

A sequence is a set of numbers that are connected in some way.

For example, a very simple sequence is
3, 6, 9, 12.

Obviously this is the three-times table, otherwise known as the multiples of three.

Most people recognise this sequence and can simply add the next three numbers: 15, 18, 21.

Example 1

Write down the next six numbers in this sequence.

$$1, 4, 9, 16, 25, -, -, -, -, -, -.$$

Explain how the sequence is made. Do this before you read any further.

We have met this sequence before – it is very important and you need to remember it. It is called the sequence of square numbers.

Another way of writing the sequence is

$$1 \times 1, \quad 2 \times 2, \quad 3 \times 3, \quad 4 \times 4, \quad 5 \times 5, \quad \ldots$$

Now it is easy to see how the sequence actually generates.

In terms of shape,

1 cm square   2 cm square   3 cm square

Again, convince yourself and then convince another person.

We have mentioned square numbers previously, have a look at the earlier mention in this chapter. It is important that you feel comfortable with this sequence.

Example 2
Can you see how this sequence is building up?

$$1, 1, 2, 3, 5, 8, -, -, -, \ldots$$

This is a very famous sequence. It was discovered by a medieval Italian mathematician called Fibonacci – it is called the 'Fibonacci sequence'.

The pattern builds up by adding together the previous two numbers.

Fibonacci

- It starts at 1.
- There is nothing in front of the first 1, so 0 + 1 = 1 and we generate the second 1.
- 1 + 1 = 2 so we generate the 2.
- In the same way, 1 + 2 = 3, 2 + 3 = 5, 3 + 5 = 8, and so on.

What is the next number in the Fibonacci sequence?

Generalising
Generalisations are simple rules that connect two sets of numbers.

We usually write these rules in the language of algebra. To get you in the mood let's play a game – it is the start–end game that we met briefly in Chapter 1.

Example 1

Start	1	2	3	4	5
End	2	4	6	8	10

This is a very simple example to get you started.
What do you do to the start numbers to get to the end numbers? Obviously you need to multiply by 2, or to double them.

So, the rule for this game is

start number × 2 = end number

This can be written this algebraically
$s \times 2 = e$, or more correctly,
$$2s = e$$

This reads as 2 multiplied by the start number (s) equals the end number (e).

We have made a simple generalisation here – we have found a rule that applies to every start number in this set of numbers and takes us to every end number.

Example 2

Start	1	2	3	4	5	6
End	3	6	9	12	15	18

What is the rule? OK you have probably found it already, but just in case, we want to talk you through a technique useful for finding rules like this.

Look at the end numbers first – here they are again.

3
6
9
12
15
18

You should have noticed that they are all going up in threes. What does this tell you? What do you know that goes up in a steady step of 3? The answer must be the three-times table.

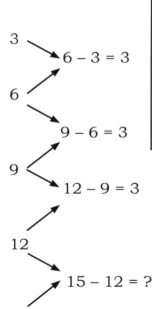

So first differences can be used to give us an early clue about a sequence and its pattern. The next thing to do is to multiply the start number by the first difference and see if this gives the end number?

3
   6 – 3 = 3
6
   9 – 6 = 3
9
   12 – 9 = 3
12
   15 – 12 = ?
15
   18 – 15 = ?
18

Does it work for every start number and take you to every end number?

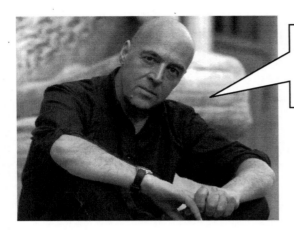

If the answer is yes, then you have found the rule that links the start and end numbers. But what if it doesn't?

Example 3

Start	1	2	3	4	5	6
End	5	8	11	14	17	20

First, work out the first differences.

$$8 - 5 = 3$$
$$11 - 8 = 3$$
$$14 - 11 = 3 \dots$$

You will agree that the first differences are 3. This gives a clue as to what to multiply the start numbers by. Now, $1 \times 3 = 3$, but the end number is 5 – what is going on?

In Example 2 in this section we had the function machine

Start $\longrightarrow$ x 3 $\longrightarrow$ End
number   number

In this example we have something slightly different

Start $\longrightarrow$ x 3 $\longrightarrow$? $\longrightarrow$ End
number   number

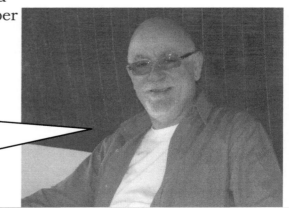

Here the first differences are 3 but that does not give us the final answer.
This number machine is a two stage process. After you have multiplied the start number by 3, you have to do something else to generate the end number.

Have you worked it out? Clearly it must be that you add 2.

So the complete operation is

Start $\xrightarrow{\hspace{2cm}}$ x 3 $\xrightarrow{\hspace{2cm}}$ +2 $\xrightarrow{\hspace{2cm}}$ End
number   number

In other words there are two operations taking place here. The first we have identified with the first differences, we now need a second operation.

Think about what this operation might be for a moment.
The question is, after we have multiplied the start number by 3, we get an interim number. What do we do with that interim number to get the end number?
Think

Start number x 3 + 2   = End number

We can write that algebraically as

$$3s + 2 = e$$

Exercise 2.3
Work out the rule for each of the sequences below.
Write your answers as algebraic equations.

1.

Start	2	3	4	5
End	10	15	20	25

2.

Start	1	2	3	4	5
End	4	7	10	13	16

3.

Start	10	11	12	13	14
End	101	111	121	131	141

4.

Start	9	10	11	12	13
End	21	23	25	27	29

5.

Start	16	17	18	19	20
End	49	52	55	58	61

6.

Start	7	8	9	10	11
End	49	64	81	100	121

7.

Start	2	4	6	8	10
End	11	21	31	41	51

8.

Start	16	17	18	19	20
End	48	51	54	57	60

9.

Start	6	7	8	9	10
End	49	57	65	73	81

10.

Start	5	10	15	20	25
End	49	99	149	199	249

11.

Start	12	13	18	19	20
End	59	64	89	94	99

12.

Start	6	7	8	9	10
End	23	26	29	32	35

Tutorial
Progress Questions

1   Write down the first four square numbers.

2   Calculate: **(a)** $\sqrt{100}$ **(b)** $\sqrt{144}$ **(c)** $\sqrt{400}$

3   What are the first four cube numbers?

4   What is the next square number after 144?

Practical Assignment
Develop a start–end game as a party game for your friends.
Try to develop the algebraic thinking of your friends.

Discussion Points
'*The more you play with numbers, the easier they become to manipulate.*'

How true is this for you? Make a comment in your journal.

3 The Power of the Index

One-Minute Overview
In order to be a successful cook or joiner, you have to have mastery of your tools. A cook who doesn't understand what a cake tin is for, or how to grease it, will not bake good cakes. A joiner who doesn't know how to put a bit in a drill will not have a long career in joinery. So the little skills are important. As a mathematician you need to understand certain skills that you will use later.

In this chapter we will look at:
- The highest common factor of two or more numbers;
- The lowest common multiple of two or more numbers;
- How to write numbers as powers;
- How to multiply and divide powers.

Directed Numbers and Indices
Numbers are either positive or negative.
Think about what happens to a bank account if you become overdrawn. If you have £3 (or Euros) in an account and take out £5, you have an overdraft of £2. In other words you owe the bank £2.
Mathematically, this can be written this as –£2.

So your account is –£2. So –2 is obviously 2 less than zero.

Another way to think of numbers is on a temperature scale.

Clearly, on a frosty winter morning when you see someone scraping ice off a car the temperature is less than zero. To be able to signify what the temperature is we need to use the negative sign.

So a temperature lower than zero has a minus sign in front of it.

How do we think of negative numbers?
When you are studying mathematics, a good way forward is to create a mental model. By this we mean something that you can recall at will, to work things out in your head.

A good way of thinking about negative numbers is to imagine a block of flats or apartments. This is only a mental model so we can be a bit silly – this block goes up through the clouds as far as the eye can see. In addition the block carries on down underground.
The ground level floor is named 'zero'. This means that the first floor above ground level is +1, the second is +2 and so on. But what do we call the first floor below

ground level? We cannot call it +1 because this refers to the first floor above ground level. So the first floor below ground level has to be –1. The second floor below is therefore –2 and the third floor is –3 and so on.

Think of this as a diagram of the block of flats or as a ladder. This will help you think through the mathematics needed.

This mental model will be useful when working with directed (positive and negative) numbers. When you are adding you are going up the block – when you are subtracting you are going down the block.

So if you were on the first floor above ground level, at +1, and you then went down 4 floors where would you be?

Mathematically this can be written

$$+1 - 4 = ?$$

You would end up at –3 of course, so +1 – 4 = –3.

Now have a go at this one. If you were on floor +5 and went down 7 floors, where would you be then? How do we write that mathematically?

If you went down 7 floors, you would be at floor –2, so mathematically +5 – 7 = –2.

What about starting underground?
Suppose you were on the fourth floor underground, in other words –4, and went up 3 floors, where would you be then and how would this operation be written?

Mathematically this is –4 + 3 = –1 so you end up on floor –1.

What about negatives minus negatives?
Let's say you were on the third floor below ground level and went down 5 floors. Where would you be then and how would this operation be written? Mathematically this would be –3 – 5 and this takes you to floor –8. So –3 – 5 –8.
Try some of these for yourself. Make sure you are clear about how to do this before you move on.

How to write directed numbers

In the earlier examples we have written 5 as +5. When we write numbers in mathematics, we either use positive or negative numbers.

If we are using negative numbers, we must always write the number with a negative sign in front of it. So negative seven is always written as –7.

Positive numbers can be written as either a number with a positive sign in front or just as a number.

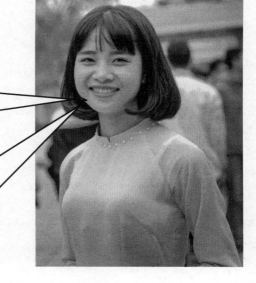

Positive numbers can be written as either a number with a positive sign in front or just as a number with no sign.

So if a number, say five, is written as just 5 then it is automatically taken to mean +5. In other words if a number has no sign in front of it, it is always a positive number.

Whenever you want to write a negative number, you must always write a negative sign in front of it.

So 5 and +5 are the same number. If you want to write negative five, you need to put a negative sign in front of it, so negative five is always written as –5.

Exercise 3.1
Calculate the value of each of these expressions.

1	$4 - 5 =$	**2**	$-3 - 5 =$	**3**	$9 - 17 =$
4	$-6 + 7 =$	**5**	$-15 + 17 =$	**6**	$12 - 17 =$
7	$5 - 12 =$	**8**	$22 - 9 =$	**9**	$-30 - 29 =$
10	$-7 - 9 =$				

Numbers and Powers

Any number on its own is to the power 1,

so 7 is the same as 7^1

9 is 9^1 and so on.

> Generally in mathematics we want to write things as simply as possible.
> Therefore there is a way of writing numbers that are multiplied by themselves.

When a number is to the power 1, we do not need to write the 1 in. So any number written to the power 1 is just that number. So 144 is 144^1 and so on.

Suppose you want to write 3×3 – the shorthand way of writing this is 3^2

So 3^2 means 3×3 and clearly 3^2 must be 9

The next one up in the sequence is 3^3 – we say this as 'three cubed' or 'three to the power three'.

$$3^3 \text{ is } 3 \times 3 \times 3.$$

Now $3 \times 3 = 9$ and then 9×3 which is 27. So $3^3 = 27$.

$$
\begin{aligned}
&3 \times 3 \times 3 \\
=\ &9 \times 3 \\
=\ &27
\end{aligned}
$$

For any power greater than 3, we say it is 'to the power of ...'.

So, for example, 5^4 is said as 'five to the power of 4'.
This worked out at $5 \times 5 \times 5 \times 5 = 625$.

it is 3 times 3 (and not 3 times 2). 3^2 is said as 'three squared' or 'three to the power of two'.

Calculators are useful for working out expressions involving powers.

On your calculator tap in '5'
Now you need to press the $x^\square$
Now press '4'. This tells the calculator that you want to work out 5^4.
Mathematically this is called raising 5 to the power 4.

Now press = and
you will see the
answer, 625.

Screenshots Courtesy
of the
Casio Corporation

Exercise 3.2
Write these numbers as powers and work them out.

1	$4 \times 4 =$	**2**	$5 \times 5 \times 5 =$	**3**	$4 \times 4 \times 4 =$
4	$9 \times 9 =$	**5**	$7 \times 7 \times 7 =$	**6**	$12 \times 12 =$
7	$3 \times 3 \times 3 \times 3 =$	**8**	$13 \times 13 =$	**9**	$14 \times 14 =$
10	$15 \times 15 =$				

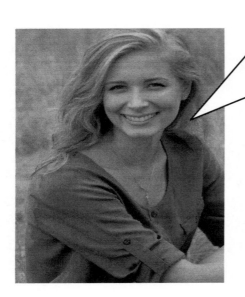

So, what is the connection with algebra? The point of algebra is often lost on many people. The point is, that it is a tool that frees up our thinking. It is a way of writing rules that apply to all the occasions we are investigating. When we deal with numbers it only applies to that one particular case.

Say Mrs Jones has three bottles of milk every day. One way of working out the total cost is to write:

total cost = three times cost of one bottle

This is algebra.

This is a word equation – what if we were to do more 'shorthanding'.

Let's call the total cost T and the cost of one bottle c. Then we can rewrite the equation as

$$T = 3c$$

It means total cost = 3 x cost of one bottle. Yay, how cool is that, algebra is in real life and not just something for egg heads!

Now we need to combine numbers and algebra. In algebra, we use the same rules that we use with numbers when working with powers.

Rule 1: Multiplying in Algebra
When multiplying, you add the powers. So, for example,

$$x \times x = x^2$$

This is because x on its own is x^1, so $x^1 \times x^1$ gives us x^{1+1} which is x^2

Any variable (a variable is shown by a letter, like x or y) that does not have a power showing is automatically to the power 1.

So y is y^1, m^1 is m and so on.

What about powers greater than 1?

The same rule applies – let's say we have to work out $m \times m^2$.

As before, we add the powers so the answer is

$$m^{(1+2)} \text{ which is } m^3$$

Exercise 3.3
Work out the answers to these expressions – give your answers in the form xy.

1	$w \times w^2 =$	**2**	$m^3 \times m^4 =$	**3**	$j^6 \times j^7 =$
4	$a^2 \times a^5 =$	**5**	$g^9 \times g^2 =$	**6**	$r \times r =$
7	$e \times e^4 =$	**8**	$d \times d^5 =$	**9**	$s^5 \times s^6 =$
10	$y^3 \times y =$				

Rule 2: Dividing in algebra
When you are dividing numbers involving powers, you subtract the powers.

So, for example,

$$t^6 \div t^3 = t^{(6-3)} = t^3$$

Remember when you are dividing you subtract the powers but only those that are the same, So, for example, $b^3 \div b^2$ or $a^3 \times a^2$ are OK because we are dealing with just the b or just the a, these letters are called the variables.

If you had $b^3 \div a$ then there are two different variables and you cannot subtract the powers.

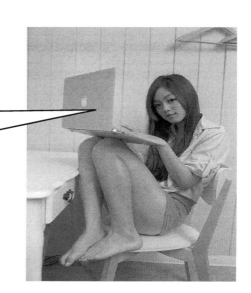

Sometimes, you will see a division written like a fraction. So, for example, you might have
$$\frac{K^8}{K^3}$$

This too is a division so you need to subtract the powers. So here, the answer is K^5

Exercise 3.4

Express each of these in the form x^y

1 $p^9 \div p^3 \quad =$ **2** $j^5 \div j^2 \quad =$ **3** $r^7 \div r^4 \quad =$

4 $w^3 \div w^2 =$ **5** $q^8 \div q^2 \quad =$ **6** $a^8 \div a^5 \quad =$

7 $m^{12} \div m^6 =$ **8** $h^{25} \div h^{24} \quad =$ **9** $y^{60} \div y^{58} =$

10 $n^2 \div n^{-4} \quad =$

What about the power zero?
One way of thinking about this is to look at this pattern.

$2^5 = 32$

$2^4 = 16$

$2^3 = 8$

$2^2 = 4$

$2^1 = 2$

$2^0 = 1$

So $10^0 = 1$ for example. Try it on your calculator – press '10' and then press your power key. You should find the answer is 1.

The same is just as true in algebra. Say you had to work out $n^3 \div n^3$

The answer would be n^0 which we have just seen is 1.
This makes sense if you think about it. What we are working out here is how many times n^3 divides into itself – clearly, the answer must be once.

Mathematics is a bit like a Windows operating system on a computer – whenever you learn to do something one way, there is usually an alternative way to do it. We could look at this calculation as $\dfrac{n^3}{n^3}$

It is still a division and the powers are still subtracted so the answer is 1.

Tutorial

Set A

1	$4 - 6 =$	**2**	$-3 - 7 =$	**3**	$11 - 17 =$
4	$-6 + 1 =$	**5**	$-15 + 13 =$	**6**	$4 \times 4 =$
7	$5 \times 5 \times 5 =$	**8**	$4 \times 4 \times 4 =$	**9**	$9 \times 9 =$
10	$7 \times 7 \times 7 \times 7 =$				

Set B

1	$w \times w^3 =$	**2**	$m^3 \times m^5 =$	**3**	$j^6 \times j^9 =$
4	$a^3 \times a^7 =$	**5**	$g^9 \times g^3 =$	**6**	$x^9 \times x^3 =$
7	$b^4 \times b^7 =$	**8**	$c^{-1} \times c^3 =$	**9**	$y^4 \times y^3 =$
10	$a^{-1} \times a^{-1} =$				

Set C

1	$p^9 \div p^2 =$	**2**	$j^5 \div j^3 =$	**3**	$r^7 \div r^3 =$
4	$w^3 \div w =$	**5**	$q^8 \div q^3 =$	**6**	$k^2 \div k^{-4} =$
7	$m^{-3} \div m^{-4} =$	**8**	$b^{-6} \div b^7 =$	**9**	$n \div n^{-4} =$
10	$a^{-3} \div a^7 =$				

Discussion points

Describe how you feel about this chapter in your journal. Do not discuss this with another person yet. Make sure you describe your own feelings adequately and make them clear and unambiguous. At this stage do not be afraid of expressing concerns about your understanding – it is quite normal to feel unsure. Certainty comes from knowledge and success.

Practical assignment

Write out a worksheet of questions in the style of the questions in this chapter and provide the answers to your questions.

4 Patterns and Rules

One-Minute Overview
Patterns and rules are important in mathematics. It means that if we can see patterns then we can make predictions of what will happen. This is the real power of mathematics and why it is so very important.

Part of your mathematical education is to learn how to investigate. This chapter includes some simple investigations for you to learn the method of investigating. In fact they are very straightforward and you will probably be surprised at how easy they are to work out – but please remember it is the method that is important.

In this chapter you will learn to:
*   Make a statement of intent, to say what you are going to do;
*   Develop investigations to build up patterns in tables.

Statement of Intent
You always start an investigation with a statement of intent. This is a statement that says what the investigation is about and how you intend to carry it out. In other words you would say,

'This investigation is about ... In it I intend to investigate what happens when I do ...'

For example, if you were given a scenario involving matchstick triangles:

Step 1: Make a statement of intent
This investigation is called Matchstick Triangles. I am going to investigate what happens when the sequence is increased, by counting the matches and the triangles.

Step 2: Collect some data
Now you would start looking at different lengths of sequences and you will have realised that you are looking at the number of triangles and the number of matches. Always make a table of results, in this case comparing the numbers of matches and triangles

Step 3: Work out the pattern
From the table work out what patterns you can see. You should to try to find an equation that links the number of matches and the number of triangles – in other words a piece of algebra that forms the general case. Think about it.

Triangles	1	2	3	4	5
Matches	3	5	7	9	11

the matchstick row always goes up by two

The fact that the number of matches always goes up by two means that this is a linear relationship (in other words, no powers greater than 1).

So now you have a hint – multiply the number of triangles (T) by 2 and what do you have to do then to get the number of matches (M) ?

$$T \times 2 \ldots? = M$$

You've probably worked out that the relationship is

(no. of triangles × 2) + 1 = no. of matches.

In algebra this is written as

$$2T + 1 = M$$

Don't forget, for each investigation you:
- Make a statement of intent,
- Draw a number of versions of the arrangement,
- Make a table of results,
- State any patterns that you notice, and finally
- Find the rule.

Investigation 1: Matchstick squares

Can you find a rule that links the number of squares with the number of matches?

Investigation 2: Houses

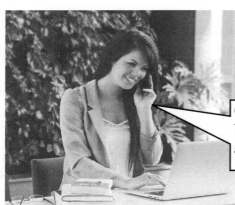

Can you find an algebraic link between the number of matches and the number of houses?

Investigation 3: Fishponds

Make the link between the number of fish and the number of slabs around the pond.

A one-fish pond

A two-fish pond

Investigation 4: Ells

In these L-shapes, compare the number (1, 2, 3) of the shape with the number of squares used. Remember – statement of intent, try out at least six, build a table and look for the rule.

Shape 1   **Shape 2**   **Shape 3**

By now you should be feeling a lot more comfortable with the idea of making generalisations in the form of simple equations. It is an important skill in mathematics.

What about non-linear relationships?

All the connections we have met at so far have been simple relationships called linear relationships. Linear relationships are algebraic expressions that when graphed form a straight line.

Now look at these results from a start–end game.

Start	1	2	3	4	5	6
End	1	4	9	16	25	36

Have you spotted the connection here? Look back at Chapter 2 if you are not sure – we have discussed these numbers before.

Now look at the first differences in the end number row – here they are again.

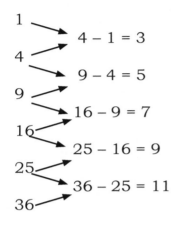

1
  4 – 1 = 3
4
  9 – 4 = 5
9
  16 – 9 = 7
16
  25 – 16 = 9
25
  36 – 25 = 11
36

So here the first differences are all different – they are 3, 5, 7, 9 and 11. But clearly there is a pattern here. We can easily predict that the next first difference in this sequence will be 13, and if you add 13 to 36 you get 49 as the end number, and obviously 7 as the start number.

So we must be on to something here – but what do we multiply the start number by to get the end number?

Let's look at the first differences again.
They are 3, 5, 7, 9, 11, 13 … Let's see if it helps, let's find the second differences

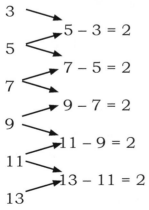

3
  5 – 3 = 2
5
  7 – 5 = 2
7
  9 – 7 = 2
9
  11 – 9 = 2
11
  13 – 11 = 2
13

This tells us something – in fact it tells us that the start number is multiplied by itself to make the end number. What is the name of the operation where we multiply a number by itself?

It is called squaring the number – so in this sequence we square the start number start number × start number = ?

This is unwieldy so let's use some algebra – letting s represent the start number

$$s \times s = ?$$

But his is also not the best final form. The best way of writing 's squared' is
$$s^2 = ?$$

OK. So now let's look at the numbers we used in this start–end game.

$$1^2 = 1 \times 1 = \mathbf{1}$$

$$2^2 = 2 \times 2 = \mathbf{4}$$

$$3^2 = 3 \times 3 = \mathbf{9}$$

$$4^2 = 4 \times 4 = \mathbf{16}$$
...

The numbers in bold type are the end numbers (e) in the original sequence.
So the relationship, or rule, is $s^2 = e$

Don't be too surprised if this is not too clear at the moment – you may need to go through it a couple of times. To help make this idea of non-linear relationships clearer let's look at another investigation.

The patterns below are made up of matchsticks.
Again we can make a table of values and look at the differences. As always, the first step is to try some out and then move on to collect data and finally look for a relationship.
 Look at how these patterns are made up.
In the first square we have 4 matches making a 1 × 1 square. In the second square we have 12 matchsticks making a 2 × 2 square. In the third square we have 24 matchsticks, giving us a 3 × 3 square.

The next stage here is to collect some data.

Remember, for a linear relationship all the first differences must be the same. In cases like this it is important to look at the second differences.

First differences	8		12		16		20		24
Second differences		4		4		4		4	

To find the rule, let's look at this table. The first row shows that there are 4 match-sticks in pattern 1. If the pattern number (n) is squared we get 1. If we then double this number we get 2.

n	m	n^2	$2n^2$
1	4	1	2
2	12	4	8
3	24	9	18
4	40	16	32
5	60	25	50

When we look at the differences we spot an immediate problem – they are not all the same. This means that there is not a linear relationship.

Here the second differences are all the same and they are a multiple of 2. This is an important clue for this investigation – it means the relationship must be quadratic –one in which the highest power is 2.

The number in the $2n^2$ column in the first row is important.

Notice that we have to add a multiple of 2 to the numbers in this column, to get the number of matchsticks. In the first row, the number in the $2n^2$ column is 2.

If we add 2×1 to this we get 4, which is the number of matchsticks in the m column.

Let's put the table in again to make the next bit clear to you.

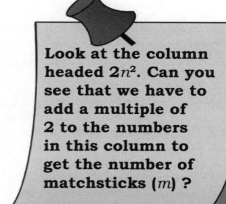

Look at the column headed $2n^2$. Can you see that we have to add a multiple of 2 to the numbers in this column to get the number of matchsticks (m) ?

n	m	n^2	$2n^2$	$2n^2 + 2n$
1	4	1	2	4
2	12	4	8	12
3	24	9	18	24
4	40	16	32	40
5	60	25	50	60

In the second row, the number in the $2n^2$ column is 8. Add 2×2 and you get 12, which is the number of matchsticks. And so it goes on.

This means that the rule connecting the number of matchsticks and the diagram number must be

$$m = 2n^2 + 2n$$

where m is the number of matchsticks and n is the pattern number.
In pattern 3 for example,

$$m = (2 \times 3^2) + (2 \times 3)$$
$$= 18 + 6$$
$$= 24$$

What about all of those x's and y's?
Algebra seems full of x's and y's where we have used mainly s and e or m and n for our equations so far.

In fact

$$s^2 = e \quad \text{and} \quad x^2 = y$$

are equivalent equations.
They describe the same operation, so instead of using s and e we could easily use x and y

Work through some of the other rows to convince yourself.
Then try convincing another person.

Here is another straightforward start–end table.

Start	1	2	3	4	5
End	1	8	27	64	125

Working out the first differences it is immediately obvious that they are different.

$$8 - 1 = 7, \qquad 27 - 8 = 19, \qquad 64 - 27 = 37, \qquad 125 - 64 = 61.$$

Now let's look at the second differences.

$$19 - 7 = 12, \qquad 37 - 19 = 18, \qquad 61 - 37 = 24.$$

Again these are all different. Let's work out the third differences.

$$18 - 12 = 6, \qquad 24 - 8 = 6.$$

They are all 6.

So this cannot be a linear (power 1) relationship or a quadratic (squared) relationship.

In fact it must be more than that.
So let's try a cubic relationship.

Here's a cubic relationship.

$$1^3 = 1 \times 1 \times 1 = \quad 1$$

$$2^3 = 2 \times 2 \times 2 = \quad 8$$

$$3^3 = 3 \times 3 \times 3 = \quad 27$$

So clearly the relationship in the start–end game we are investigating here is cubic and, in fact, it is the series of cube numbers.

Writing this algebraically this gives us the relationship

$$s^3 = e$$

Note that this could be written as $x^3 = y$

Investigation 5: Frogs

The spotted frogs have to get to where the plain frogs are, and the plain frogs to where the spotted frogs are – but there are some rules to be obeyed.

- Only one frog can move at a time.
- A frog can hop onto the lillypad space between the frogs.
- A frog can hop over another frog into an empty lillypad space.

The problem to solve is, with three frogs on each side, what is the minimum number of moves needed to get all the spotted frogs to where the plain frogs are, and all the plain frogs to where the spotted frogs are?

What about 4 frogs on each side?
    5 frogs?   6 frogs?   10 frogs?

Tutorial
Progress questions
Answer the following questions in your journal.

1 What is a linear relationship ?

2 What is a quadratic relationship?

3 What is a cubic relationship?

4 Explain how the method of first differences works.

5 Explain how we can spot a quadratic relationship using the method of second differences.

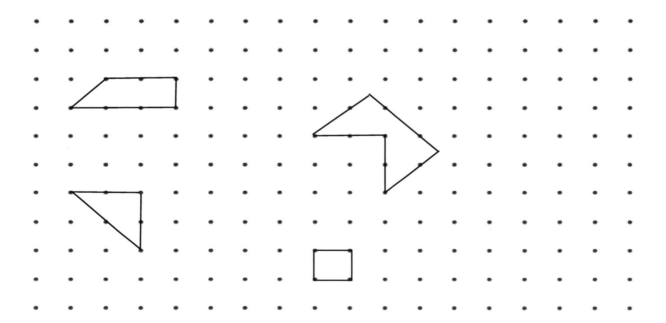

Practical Assignment
Investigate the relationship (rule) in the following situation.

- Make some dotty shapes with no dots inside – like the ones in the diagram.
- Find the area of each shape and the number of dots on its perimeter.
- Make a table of results with area in one column and the number of dots in the other.
- Label each column with a letter – either x or y.
- Formulate an equation that describes the relationship.
- Generalise – find a rule that connects the number of dots on the perimeter and the area.
- Now do the same for shapes with one dot inside and two dots and so on.

5 How to Solve Linear Equations

One-Minute Overview

Equations are statements written in the language of algebra. They are algebraic expressions and contain the '=' symbol just once, meaning the two sides must be equal. In this chapter, you will learn how to solve an equation with:

- An unknown on one side;
- An unknown on both sides;
- An unknown on both sides & a negative coefficient;
- Brackets;
- Fractions.

What is an Equation?

An equation is an algebraic expression which contains the = symbol just once, meaning that the two sides must be equal.

$$So\ x + 4 = 10\ is\ an\ equation -$$

it reads as 'an unknown number + 4 gives the answer 10'. Clearly that number must be 6.

The important thing is to learn the method for solving equations, because this will form the foundation for tackling harder equations.

Note that it is standard practice when writing a set of equations on successive lines to ensure that the equal signs line up underneath each other.

How to solve an equation with an unknown on one side

We will call this a type one equation.
Let's look at the example we just used.

We know that the answer is 6, but how do we get there?

$$x + 4 = 10$$

We have already agreed that this means

$$'a\ number + 4 = 10'.$$

If we take 4 away from the left-hand side it will leave us with just the number x

But to keep the equation in balance, we need to take 4 from the right-hand side as well. So the next line is

$$x + 4 - 4 = 10 - 4$$

On the left-hand side, $4 - 4 = 0$, so that must mean we are only left with the x.

So the next line is

$$x = 6$$

and this is the final answer.

It is always a good idea to do a check at the end. If we put the 6 back into the original equation we get $6 + 4 = 10$ and we know we have solved the equation correctly.

Review
Look at what we have done. The left-hand side had a +4 so we subtracted 4 from the left-hand side and therefore had to subtract 4 from the right-hand side. We 'undid' the equation by subtracting 4 from both sides. Manipulating an equation like this leaves the unknown on its own on one side of the equation. In algebra this is known as isolating the variable.

Try this one.

Since we have $y + 7$ on the left, we need to undo the left-hand side by taking 7 away.

$$y + 7 = 21$$

$$y + 7 - 7 = 21 - 7$$

This will leave us with the y. But we must also take 7 away from the right-hand side.

$$y = 14$$

Check: substitute the final answer into the original equation.
Do this by taking out the y, putting in the 14 and then making the judgement as to whether it makes sense or not.

Substituting gives
    $14 + 7 = 21$, so we know that $y = 14$ must be correct.

Exercise 5.1
Work out the value of the variable in each of these expressions.

1 $z + 5 = 10$ **2** $y + 8 = 19$ **3** $v + 8 = 15$

4 $m + 4 = 7$ **5** $f + 8 = 12$ **6** $d + 15 = 35$

7 $a + 4 = 16$ **8** $r + 23 = 51$ **9** $a + 20 = 119$

10 $p + 9 = 90$

What about equations with subtractions in them?
In the examples above, we undid an equation by subtracting from both sides.

This was because the equations were all of the form

> an unknown + a number = another number.

Example 1

Let's look at the equation
$$x - 7 = 15$$

Here the form is different – it is

> an unknown – a number = another number.

To undo this type of equation you need to add instead of subtract.

So, for example, look at the equation
$$x - 7 = 15.$$
Now add 7 to both sides,

$$x - 7 + 7 = 15 + 7$$

Since $-7 + 7 = 0$, the equation now becomes

$$x = 22.$$
Check: Putting 22 in to the original equation, we get $22 - 7 = 15$, just what we wanted. So x = 22 must be the correct answer.

Example 2
$$y - 9 = 27$$

Undo the equation by adding 9 to both sides
Check: $36 - 9 = 27$. So we know that
$$y - 9 + 9 = 27 + 9$$
$$y = 36 \text{ is correct.}$$

here - 9 + 9 = 0, so leaves us with y

This can often cause panic because of the way the equation is presented. However, with a bit of clear thinking this does not have to be a problem. As before, we first 'tidy up' the numbers. To do this we subtract 14 from both sides.

Example 3

This one has a slight twist.

$$14 - k = 20$$

$$14 - k - 14 = 20 - 14$$

$$-k = 6$$

Returning to the problem – we multiply throughout by −1 to get

$$k = -6$$

Check: putting this into the original equation gives

$$14 - (-6) = 14 + 6 = 20$$

so we know we are correct.

Multiplying throughout an equation by -1
Think about equations like

$$-y = 5$$

We don't want −y, we want y. To do this the technique used is to multiply throughout by −1.

$$-y \times -1 = y \text{ and } 5 \times -1 = -5$$

So after multiplying by −1, the equation becomes

$$y = -5$$

This is a useful technique for changing equations from a negative form to a positive form.

Exercise 5.2

Work out the value of the variable in each of these expressions.

1 $x - 7 = 30$ **2** $v - 8 = 19$ **3** $c - 6 = 9$

4 $m - 30 = 17$ **5** $k - 40 = 15$ **6** $a - 8 = 12$

7 $l - 9 = 45$ **8** $d - 60 = 50$ **9** $q - 90 = 100$

10 $n - 25 = 250$ **11** $12 - k = 10$ **12** $14 - f = 20$

13 $10 - 10k = 100$ **14** $17h - 6 = 28$ **15** $6 - 12f = 18$

What about equations with multiplications in them?

Multiplication in algebra is indicated by putting two terms side by side.

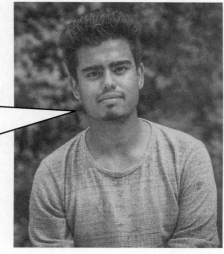

At this stage it doesn't matter what x is, we are simply trying to work out a method for undoing the multiplication.

Remember when we did earlier type one equations, we undid addition by subtracting.

This works because, for example, $3 - 3 = 0$.

So $3x$ means $3 \times x$

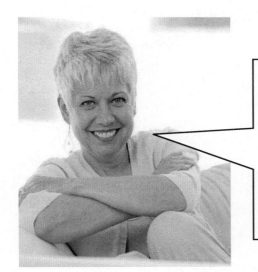

So can we make it work with multiplication? Pick any number and multiply it by 4.

Now divide your answer by 4, what happens?

Does this always happen? Make sure that you convince yourself, before you go any further.

How does this work in an equation?

Look at $3x = 12$.

This equation is saying

$\qquad$ 3 times an unknown number = 12

The unknown number must be 4 – but we need to understand how to do this algebraically.

We have already said that ÷ and × are opposites. Let's look at this in action.

So, dividing by the same thing that we multiplied by allows us to undo a multiplication.

Here we multiplied 12 by 4 and then divided the result by 4 – leaving the 12 unchanged.

Try some more of these out for yourself – convince yourself first and then convince another person.

How does this work in algebra?

It is just the same principle.
Look at this term,

$$\frac{3x}{3} = \frac{12}{3}$$

$3x$ is being divided by 3

This does not change the value of x, so we can literally cross the 3s out.

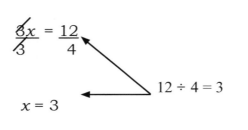

$$\frac{\cancel{3}x}{\cancel{3}} = \frac{12}{4}$$

$12 \div 4 = 3$

$x = 3$

Make sure you are clear what is happening here. We are saying on the left hand side that
$3 \div 3 = 1$
then $1 \times x = x$

This leaves us with x. This is the called the method of cancelling – it only works when you are multiplying (or dividing) by the same number.

Example 1

So let's go back to our starting example,

$$3x = 12$$

The technique is to divide both sides by whatever is in front of the unknown (variable) – this is called the coefficient of x.

So here we divide both sides by 3 and the equation becomes

$$\frac{\cancel{3}x}{\cancel{3}} = \frac{12}{3}$$

The 3s on the left-hand side cancel and $12 \div 3 = 4$

$$\text{so } x = 4.$$

Notice how we divided both sides of the equation by the same number, using the golden rule that you never operate on one side of the equation without doing exactly the same thing on the other side.

Don't forget the check: putting $x = 4$ into $3x$ we get

$$3 \times 4 = 12$$

Example 2

The equation is

$$5y = 100$$

$$\frac{\cancel{5}y}{\cancel{5}} = \frac{100}{5}$$

$$y = 20$$

The 5s on the left-hand side cancel and since $100 \div 5 = 20$,

Check: Putting $y = 20$ into $5y$

$$5y = 5 \times 20$$
$$5y = 100$$

so we divide both sides by the number in front of the un known, in this case 5 (remember this is the coefficient of y)

Exercise 5.3

Work out the value of the variable in each of these expressions.

1 $6y = 36$ **2** $7m = 42$ **3** $18n = 36$

4 $9y = 27$ **5** $14y = 28$ **6** $12t = 144$

7 $10u = 70$ **8** $100r = 100$ **9** $25f = 50$

10 $4d = 16$

What about equations with divisions in them?

Just as with multiplication, we have to do the opposite.
Here we have to multiply to undo the equation.

For example, with

$$\frac{x}{4} = 7$$

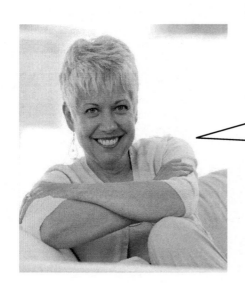

Think about it, $x/_4$ means a quarter (or fourth in the USA) of x, so if we want a whole x, we need to multiply by 4

$$\frac{4 \times x}{4} = 4 \times 7$$

we mutiply both sides by 4

$$\frac{\cancel{4}x}{\cancel{4}} = 28$$

$$x = 28$$

Check: putting $x = 28$ into

$$\frac{x}{4} = 7$$

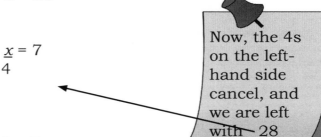

Now, the 4s on the left-hand side cancel, and we are left with 28

it becomes

$$\frac{28}{4} = 7$$

Since this is true. i.e. $28 \div 4 = 7$, we know we must have the right answer.

Once again, convince yourself about this – make sure you understand it. Try talking it through with another person – it really does help you to understand the mathematics.

Exercise 5.4
Work out the value of the variable in each of these expressions.

1. $\dfrac{x}{3} = 9$

2. $\dfrac{t}{7} = 3$

3. $\dfrac{m}{5} = 8$

4. $\dfrac{y}{6} = 8$

5. $\dfrac{t}{12} = 5$

6. $\dfrac{a}{2} = 2$

7. $\dfrac{y}{2} = 3$

8. $\dfrac{p}{3} = 11$

9. $\dfrac{y}{6} = 15$

10. $\dfrac{k}{2} = 5$

You now have all the skills needed to solve simple equations with one unknown. What you may not have realised yet is that they occur in all sorts of combinations.

For example,

$$2x + 4 = 7.$$

Here you have to undo the addition and then undo the multiplication between the 2 and the x. So, in stages, taking 4 from both sides

$$2x + 4 - 4 = 7 - 4$$

The bolded part shows the original equation – all we have done is take 4 from both sides. This gives

$$2x = 3$$

Now undo the $2x$ by dividing both sides by 2

and so

$$x = 1.5.$$

Check: putting $x = 1.5$ in $2x + 4$ produces 7 – just as it should do.

Remember, undo the equation by doing the opposite and always do exactly the same thing to both sides of the equation.

Exercise 5.5
Work out the value of the variable in each of these expressions.

1	$2x + 5 = 9$	**2**	$4x + 6 = 14$	**3**	$5f + 9 = 54$
4	$5x + 7 = 37$	**5**	$6r + 8 = 50$	**6**	$8t + 9 = 17$
7	$9p + 1 = 82$	**8**	$7r + 1 = 15$	**9**	$8y + 6 = 70$
10	$6r + 4 = 40$				

How to solve equations containing negative numbers
For example $4x - 13 = -1$, but don't worry – you have already seen these before. So for

$$4x - 13 = -1,$$

$$4x - 13 + 13 = -1 + 13$$

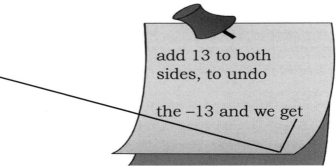

add 13 to both sides, to undo

the −13 and we get

Look at what has happened, we have changed an equation from a type we didn't know about, to one we do know about. We have seen this type before. So now you just need to solve this in the same way as you did earlier. Have a go at it first and then check your answer with the one below.

You should have found that $x = 3$.

Check: putting $x = 3$ into $4x - 13$ gives -1, just as it should do.

 Understanding Algebra

Exercise 5.6

Work out the value of the variable in each of these expressions.

1 $2x - 3 = 1$ **2** $4x - 8 = 28$ **3** $5f - 5 = 30$

4 $5x - 10 = 25$ **5** $6r - 6 = 30$ **6** $8t - 7 = 1$

7 $9p - 1 = 17$ **8** $7r - 1 = 20$ **9** $8y - 2 = 78$

10 $6r - 4 = 50$

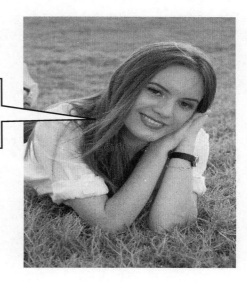

Remember what we said in the last section; change the equation into a type you are already familiar with and know how to solve.

How to solve equations with an unknown on both sides of the equation

Look at this equation – it has an x on both sides

$$4x + 4 = x + 16.$$

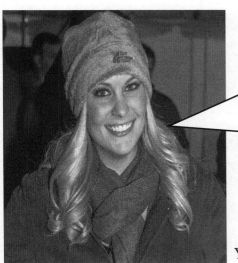

Tackle it by undoing the x term with the lowest coefficient, remember the coeffiecient is the number in front of the x.

Since x is smaller than $4x$, undo this one first. So it becomes

Now you have it in a form that you should recognise and know how to solve. So have a go and solve it now – then check with the answer below.

You should have found that $x = 4$.

Check: putting $x = 4$ into

$$4x + 4 = x + 16 \qquad \text{gives 20 on both sides, which is fine.}$$

Remember, this is all to do with changing equations from a form that you don't know what to do with straightaway, into a form that you are confident with and have the techniques to tackle.

Health Warning

Some students develop the habit of writing equations as they think. Remember, you only use one equals sign on each level of working.

For example, presented with

$$x + 3 = 4 \qquad \text{they say take 3 away from both sides, so that}$$

$$x + 3 - 3 = 4 - 3$$

$$x + 3 - 3 = 4 - 3 = 1.$$

The correct way to write this calculation out is:

$$x + 3 = 4$$

$$x + 3 - 3 = 4 - 3$$

$$x = 1$$

Exercise 5.7

Work out the value of the variable in each of these expressions .

1 $5x - 4 = 4x + 1$ **2** $9y + 17 = 14y + 7$

3 $4t + 5 = 6t - 3$ **4** $8a + 5 = 3a + 50$

5 $6y + 7 = 7y$

What about brackets?

Brackets are commonly used in mathematics.
Usually brackets tell you to deal with the numbers
inside the brackets first.
So, say you had

$$3 \times (4 + 5)$$

This means do the 4 + 5 sum first, and then multiply the answer by 3. So the answer you should get is 27.

But in algebra things are done slightly differently! In algebra brackets mean that you have to multiply.

So

$3(x + 4)$ means do $3 \times x$ first and then do $+3 \times 4$ giving $3x + 12$.

In other words,

$3(x + 4) = 3x + 12$

This is called expanding brackets and we will examine this in more detail in the next chapter.

Exercise 5.8
Expand these brackets.

1 $8(c + 6) =$ **2** $2(a + 3) =$ **3** $6(t + 5) =$

4 $5(u - 8) =$ **5** $3(r - 9) =$ **6** $6(y - 7) =$

7 $4(y - 5) =$ **8** $3(2t - 6) =$ **9** $5(7y - 6) =$

10 $7(7t + 7) =$

How to solve equations with fractions

The denominator is the lower part of the fraction. You need to think of denominators as dividers.

So to undo the division when the unknown is in the denominator you need to multiply.

Look at this example.
$$\frac{4}{x} = 5$$

This reads as '4 divided by an unknown equals 5'. The rule is to multiply both sides of the equation by what is in the denominator.

So here
$$\frac{4}{x} \times x = 5 \times x$$

Look at what happens to the left-hand side

$$\frac{4\cancel{x}}{\cancel{x}} = 5x$$

The x's cancel and notice what this does– it changes the equation to a form we have already worked on.

Now the equation reads
$$4 = 5x$$

and all we have to do solve it use the rules we met earlier. Divide both sides by 5 and do the cancelling

$$\frac{4}{5} = \frac{\cancel{5}x}{\cancel{5}}$$

so that gives us
$$\frac{4}{5} = x$$

or
$$x = \frac{4}{5}$$

Unsure about cancelling?

Look at this, $3x = 18$.

This reads '3 times an unknown number equals 18'.

We don't want 3 times the unknown, we want the unknown on its own.
So we divide both sides by 3

$$\frac{3x}{3} = \frac{18}{3}$$

We are now multiplying and dividing the x by the same number.

What happens when you multiply and divide a number by the same number? You are left with the original number. That's why we can cancel the threes on the left-hand side leaving x on its own.

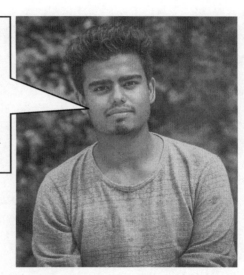

$$\frac{\cancel{3}x}{\cancel{3}} = \frac{18}{3}$$

On the left hand side the 3's cancel, the 3 in the denominator (bottom) of the fraction, goes into the 3 in the numerator (top) once. Then 1 multiplied by x is x. On the right hand side, 18 divided by 3 = 6.

$x = 6$

Tutorial
Progress questions

1 $k + 7 = 10$

2 $y + 9 = 19$

3 $v + 2 = 15$

4 $m + 3 = 7$

5 $f + 7 = 12$

6 $x - 10 = 30$

7 $v - 7 = 19$

8 $c - 8 = 9$

9 $m - 31 = 17$

10 $k - 41 = 15$

11 $7y = 49$

12 $7m = 35$

13 $6n = 36$

14 $9y = 27$

15 $14y = 28$

16 $\dfrac{x}{3} = 9$

17 $\dfrac{m}{5} = 8$

18 $\dfrac{t}{7} = 3$

19 $\dfrac{y}{6} = 8$

20 $\dfrac{t}{12} = 5$

21 $8(c + 6) = 88$

22 $2(a + 3) = 18$

23 $6(t + 5) = 42$

24 $5(u - 8) = 45$

25 $3(r - 9) = 27$

Discussion point
Explain the techniques you have met in this chapter to another person. Convince yourself first and then convince them.

Study tip
Use your journal to record an example of each of these techniques in action. Write out a model solution on the left-hand side of the page with a black pen, and then use a red pen to write instructions on the right-hand side. You could use this as material to help the explanation suggested above.

6 Brackets and Factors

One-Minute Overview

In this chapter we are going to look at how to use brackets and factors. The first part will deal with expanding brackets. Then we will look at factors.

In this chapter you will learn:
* About simple expansion of brackets and factorising;
* About the difference of two squares;
* How to factorise quadratic expressions;
* How to complete the square as a mechanism for factorising;
* How change the subject of a formula;
* How to deal with algebraic fractions.

How to Expand Brackets

Brackets in algebra often cause confusion – but there is nothing to fear here.

Let's look at a simple example. Suppose we want to expand $(x + 4)(x + 3)$. We can use the rectangle diagram to help.

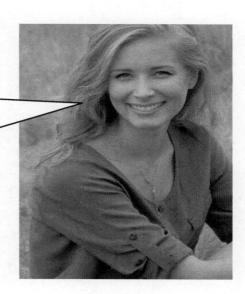

Now look at the area of each of the rectangles. The top left rectangle is actually a square. We know this because both sides have the same length (x).
OK, so how do we calculate the area of a square?

We use the simple formula, area $= l^2$

So the area of the top left square is x^2

Now let's do the same with the top right rectangle –

you should find that the area is $4x$

The bottom left rectangle comes out at $3x$ and

the bottom right comes out at 12 (4 × 3)

x^2	$4x$
$3x$	12

We can now put these separate areas together as

$$x^2 + 4x + 3x + 12$$

Notice that the two middle terms are like terms and so can be added together.

So the final answer

is $x^2 + 7x + 12$

This means that

$$(x + 4)(x + 3) = x^2 + 7x + 12$$

After some practice, you will find that you will be able to do this expansion without the diagrams –but don't worry about using them at this stage.
If they help you to learn, that is all that matters.

A word on like and unlike terms

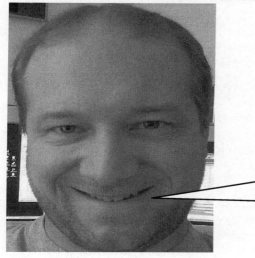

In algebra, like terms are terms that are the same and can be operated on. By 'operated' we mean you can add, subtract, multiply or divide. This is not as strange as it might first appear.

In real life, you cannot add hens and elephants. If you have three hens and seven elephants, you cannot combine them to get ten hen-elephants or ten-elephant-hens.

Like Terms

In algebra we use the noun 'variable' to apply to values in equations – we show these variables as letters of the alphabet. So, in short, you can add or subtract, multiply or divide letters that are the same. If the letters are not the same you cannot operate on them. So in algebra

$$a + a = 2a$$

$$b + b + b = 3b$$

Unlike Terms

Notice that uppercase letters and lowercase letters do not represent the same variable

so B is not the same as b

Similarly

x^2 is not the same as x (think about it, $x^2 = x \times x$)

When you multiply unlike variables, they are written side by side, so

$x \times y$ is written as xy,

and a divided by b is usually written as the fraction $\dfrac{a}{b}$

Multiplying by 1

We do not write $1x$ or $1a$ or $1b$.

If the variable is a letter on its own, then it is automatically taken as just one of them – so $1b$ should just be written as b, $1a$ should just be written as a and so on.

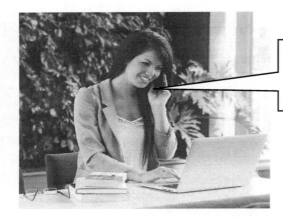

Make a journal entry on like and unlike terms. Be clear in your own mind what these mean and how to use this information in your own algebra.

Here is another example showing how to expand brackets using $(x + 1)(x + 3)$.

	x	$+1$
x	x^2	x
$+3$	$3x$	3

So $(x + 1)(x + 3) = x^2 + x + 3x + 3$,
but remember we need to tidy up the middle two terms.
$$= x^2 + 4x + 3$$

Another way to do this, is to simply multiply out the brackets. This is often known as the 'smiley face' method. The secret is that everything in the second bracket is multiplied by everything in the first bracket

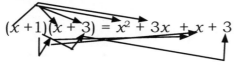

$(x + 1)(x + 3) = x^2 + 3x + x + 3$

$(x + 1)(x + 3) = x^2 + 4x + 3$

here the $4x$ comes from $3x + x$ in the line above

Exercise 6.1
Expand the brackets and simplify these expressions.

1 $(x + 2)(x + 3) =$ **2** $(x + 1)(x + 5) =$

3 $(y + 3)(y + 4) =$ **4** $(x - 2)(x + 5) =$

5 $(x + 5)(x - 3) =$ **6** $(m + 7)(m - 3) =$

7 $(v + 4)(v - 3) =$ **8** $(z - 8)(z - 7) =$

9 $(a - 7)(a - 5) =$ **10** $(d + 6)(d + 7) =$

Expanding brackets with coefficients greater than one

The coefficient is the number in front of the letter, so c on its own has a coefficient of 1, (we mentioned this earlier) as indeed does x, y or any other variable on its own. In this section we will be dealing with expanding expressions such as

$$(4x + 5)(x - 2) = ?$$

You have a go at this and compare your answer with ours below.

OK. how well did you get on?

The secret here is to expand the x's first and then do the numbers.

First, multiply the $4x$ in the first bracket by everything in the second bracket.

$$(4x + 5)(x - 2) =$$

That gives two terms, $4x \times x$ and $4x \times -2$

Then multiply the $+5$ in the first bracket by everything in the second bracket.

$$(4x + 5)(x - 2) =$$

That gives two more terms, $+5 \times x$ and $+5 \times -2$.

Adding these new terms together gives

$$4x^2 - 8x + 5x - 10.$$ As in the earlier examples we tidy up the middle two terms giving final expansion

$$(4x + 5)(x - 2) = 4x^2 - 3x - 10.$$

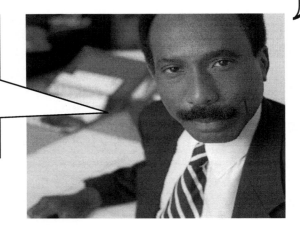

Use your journal to make a note of what we have just done.
Draw the diagram and annotate it.
Use colour on the diagram as this stimulates the brain. In your own words explain what we have done and how we used the diagram to get to the final answer

Exercise 6.2
Expand the brackets and simplify these expressions.

1 $(2x + 1)(x - 4) =$

2 $(3x + 4)(x - 1) =$

3 $(3d - 4)(4d - 3) =$

4 $(3f - 5)(4f + 6) =$

5 $(7g - 5)(g - 6) =$

6 $(4 - x)(6 - x) =$

7 $(6 - y)(7 - y) =$

8 $(9 + t)(t + 4) =$

9 $(14 - y)(12 + 2y) =$

10 $3(4y - 3)(5y + 4) =$

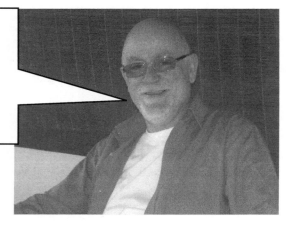

Here is another type of expression which includes brackets, $(x + 5)^2$
How is this type of expression expanded?

Think about what 'squared' means – we looked at this earlier in the book.

Expanding Squares

Squaring means multiplying something by itself.
So $(x + 5)^2$ means $(x + 5)(x + 5)$

– so we work this out exactly
in the same way that we worked out the earlier type of bracket expression.

Therefore, $(x + 5)^2 = (x + 5)(x + 5)$

$$= x^2 + 5x + 5x + 25$$

$$= x^2 + 10x + 25$$

Exercise 6.3
Expand the brackets and simplify these expressions.

1 $(x + 4)^2 =$ **2** $(f + 5)^2 =$

3 $(x - 3)^2 =$ **4** $(d + 7)^2 =$

5 $(m + 2)^2 =$ **6** $(g - 3)^2 =$

7 $(x + 1)^2 + (x - 2)^2 =$ **8** $(k + 6)^2 + (k + 8)^2 =$

9 $(y - 4)^2 + (y + 6)^2 =$ **10** $(x + 2)^2 + (3x - 4)^2 =$

Sometimes we have a number in front of the bracket
say $5(x + 7)^2$, here we need to use square brackets

so
$5(x + 7)^2 = 5[(x+7)(x+7)]$ work out inside the
square bracket first

$= 5(x^2 + 14x + 49)$ Now multiply
throughout by 5

$= 5x^2 \ 70x + 245$

Exercise 6.4
Expand the brackets and simplify these expressions.

1 $(x + 3)^2 =$ **2** $(x + 1)^2 =$

3 $(x - 5)^2 =$ **4** $(3x + 2)^2 =$

5 $(4y + 1)^2 =$ **6** $4(x + 6)^2 =$

7 $2(x + 1)^2 =$ **8** $6(x + 3)^2 =$

9 $5(x + 2)^2 =$ **10** $5(y + 7)^2 =$

Factors and Factorising

Remember, in numbers, a factor is a number that goes into another number without a remainder.

In algebra, this means finding what to multiply to get an expression. It is splitting an expression into a multiplication of simpler algebra expressions. In the U.K. this is called factorising, in America it is called factoring.

Example 1

How do we factorise $6y + 4$?

We need the highest common factor of 6 and 4. This means we are looking for the largest number that goes into both 6 and 4, it turns out to be 2.

So we now have

$$6y + 4 = 2(? + ?)$$

Now, what do we need to multiply 2 by, to make $6y$? That must be $3y$ so we have the first term inside the bracket

$$6y + 4 = 2(3y + ?)$$

Now we need to work out the last term in the bracket. Ask yourself 'what do I need to multiply the 2 outside the bracket with to generate the +4?'
Obviously it must be +2, so that gives us the final term and the answer.

$$6y + 4 = 2(3y + 2)$$

Factorising (or factoring in the US) is the opposite of expanding brackets. It is the process of identifying the factors that make up a term – we are 'putting brackets in'.

Notice that here, when factorising, we have reversed the expansion technique that we looked at earlier in this chapter.

Here we need to look at both the numbers and the letters. Ask yourself 'what is the largest number and which common letter can be extracted?'

Example 2

How do we factorise $3xy + 6y^2$?

- the largest factor (number) that goes into both 3 and 6 is **3**
- the largest algebraic term that goes into both xy and y^2 is **y**

So the biggest common factor to extract is **3y**
This gives

$$3xy + 6y^2 = \mathbf{3y}\,(\,?\,+\,?\,)$$

Now ask yourself 'what do you need to multiply $3y$ by to make $3xy$?'

The answer must be x so the first term in the bracket is x

$$3xy + 6y^2 = 3y\,(x + \,?\,)$$

Now ask yourself 'what do I multiply $3y$ by to generate $6y^2$?

Now $2 \times 3 = 6$ and $y \times y = y^2$ so the term must be $2y$.

So the answer is

$$3xy + 6y^2 = 3y\,(x + 2y)$$

Example 3

Factorise $4x^2 + 5x$

The common factor is x – there is an x^2 in the first term and an x in the second term, so we can extract an x from both

$x\,(\,? + ?\,)$

Again, what do we need to multiply x by to get the $4x^2$ term? The answer must be $4x$

So this is what it looks like at the moment

$x\,(\,4x + ?\,)$

Now we need to generate the $5x$ term – what do we need to multiply the x outside the bracket by to make $5x$?

Clearly the answer is 5.

So the final answer is

$$4x^2 + 5x = x\,(\,4x + 5\,)$$

Exercise 6.5

Complete the factorising for the following – some have been started for you.

1 $8x + 6y = 2(\,4x + ?\,)$ **2** $9y + 12z = 3\,(\,? + 4z\,)$

3 $10x + 5y = 5(\,? + y\,)$ **4** $4a + 16b = 4(\,? + ?\,)$

5 $10x + 15y = (\ \ + \ \ )$ **6** $9x - 27y\ =$

7 $27x - 81y =$ **8** $30a - 25b =$

9 $6x^2 - 15x =$ **10** $7m^2 - 49m =$

The Difference of Two Squares

Remember, you get a square number when you multiply a number by itself.

```
      *              * *
  1 x 1 = 1          * *
                   2 x 2 = 4
```

$1 \times 1 = 1$, so 1 is a square number; $2 \times 2 = 4$ so 4 is a square number.

In the same way, in algebraic terms can be square terms, for example x^2
For example, in the expression

$\qquad\qquad m^2 - 25$ both terms are squares and it is a subtraction – therefore it is a difference of two squares.

 Understanding Algebra

So How do we Factorise a Difference of Two Squares?

Here is the rule

difference of two squares = ($\sqrt{}$1st term + $\sqrt{}$2nd term)($\sqrt{}$1st term – $\sqrt{}$2nd term)

Remember, $\sqrt{}$ means 'the square root of'.

So...

$$m^2 - 25 = (m + 5)(m - 5)$$

Convince yourself by expanding the brackets on the right-hand side. This should take you back to the expression on the left-hand side.

Exercise 6.6
Factorise the following expressions using the difference of squares method.

1 $x^2 - y^2 =$

2 $t^2 - y^2 =$

3 $a^2 - b^2 =$

4 $a^2 - 1 =$

5 $9g^2 - h^2 =$

6 $16x^2 - y^2 =$

7 $x^2 - \frac{1}{4} =$

8 $9a^2 - 16b^2 =$

9 $9y^2 - z^2 =$

10 $16a^2 - \frac{9}{25}b^2 =$

Squaring Negatives
Squaring negative terms can cause confusion, but there is a simple rule to follow:
*   multiplying two terms with signs that are the same gives a positive answer;
*   multiplying two terms with signs that are different gives a negative answer.

So   +   ×   +   =   +
        –   ×   –   =   +
        +   ×   –   =   –

        –   ×   +   =   –

How to factorise quadratic expressions
Quadratic expressions are those in which the highest power is 2. This means there is a squared term in there somewhere.

Investigating a × b = 0
Think about a multiplication where the answer is zero – what does that tell you about the terms in the multiplication?

Try 1×0 or 2×0 or anything times zero and you will always get zero. We will come back to use this fact when solving quadratics by facto

Remember, part of learning mathematics is to convince yourself and then convince another person.

Remember factorising means rewriting the expression as a product of two factors. That means two things that are multiplied. Remember, factorisation it is the reverse process of expansion.

Factorising quadratics
Remember a quadratic is an expression that is usually of the form
$$ax^2 + bx + c$$

Here, a is a number not equal to zero and b and c are also numbers.

Factorising Quadratics with Positive Coefficients
First we are going to consider examples in which b and c are both positive numbers.

Example 1
This means we want to rewrite expressions
such as

$$x^2 + 5x + 6 \text{ in the form } (x + ?)(x + ?)$$

where the question marks are replaced by whole numbers.

We can find these numbers by examining each of the coefficients (the numbers in front of the x'

So $x^2 + 4x + 6$ is a quadratic and so is $3x^2 + 2x + 15$

Any algebraic expresssion where the highest power is 2 is a quadratic.

Coefficients of 1

Remember, when a coefficient is 1 we do not write the coefficient in front of the variable (letter).

So when we have x this means that there is only one x here.

So, for example, the coefficient of x^2 in

$$x^2 + 5x + 6 \quad \text{is } 1$$

Remember we are changing the quadratic to the form where it has factors in two brackets

i.e. $\qquad x^2 + 5x + 6$ changes to the form $(x +/- \, ?)(x +/- \, ?)$

How to Factorise Quadratic Expressions

Quadratic expressions are those in which the highest power is 2. This means there is a squared term in there somewhere.

Remember a quadratic is an expression that is usually of the form

$$ax^2 + bx + c$$

Here, a is a number not equal to zero and b and c are also numbers.

Let's look at $x^2 + 5x + 6$

The coefficient of x^2 in $x^2 + 5x + 6$ is 1.

So the first step here is to check that the coefficient of x^2 in the product of

$(x + ?)(x + ?)$ is also 1.

$(x + \ ?)(x + ?)$

The diagram shows that the coefficients do agree.

The constant term in the original expression is 6 and this gives a good clue about the two numbers that are going to replace the question marks in the factorisation above. It means that we need to look for factors of 6 – two numbers that multiply together to give 6.

This means that we need to consider 1 and 6, and 3 and 2.

But we also need these numbers to add up to the coefficient of the x term in the expression, namely 5.

This means the factors we choose must be 3 and 2. So the full factorisation is,
$$x^2 + 5x + 6 = (x + 3)(x + 2)$$

We can check this by expanding the brackets and it should take us back to the start.

$$(x + 3)(x + 2) = x^2 + 2x + 3x + 6$$
$$= x^2 + 5x + 6$$

So, we need to:
- Check the coefficient of x^2.
- Look at the constant term, this is the last one in the quadratic, the number.
- Choose the correct factors by comparing with the coefficient of x.

Check: expand the right-hand side of the equation and you should find it takes you back to the left-hand side.

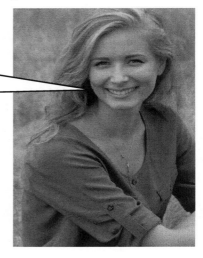

Example 2

$$x^2 + 5x + 4 = (? + ?)(? + ?)$$

- Checking the coefficient of x^2 shows it to be 1.

- The constant term is 4 which has factors of
  2×2 and 1×4.

- The factors chosen should add up to make 5, the coefficient of x.
  So the factors must be 1 and 4.

This means that

$$x^2 + 5x + 4 = (x + 1)(x + 4)$$

Check: expand the right-hand side of the equation and you should find it takes you back to the left-hand side.

© 2018 Graham Lawler. Understanding Algebra

Exercise 6.7
Factorise these quadratic expressions.

1 $x^2 + 9x + 20 =$ **2** $x^2 + 12x + 35 =$

3 $x^2 + 17x + 60 =$ **4** $x^2 + 10x + 21 =$

5 $x^2 + 16x + 15 =$ **6** $x^2 + 8x + 15 =$

7 $x^2 + 11x + 18 =$ **8** $x^2 + 12x + 11 =$

9 $x^2 + 8x + 12 =$ **10** $x^2 + 14x + 45 =$

This section shows us that quadratics of the form $x^2 + bx + c$ can be factorised and that they take the form $(x + \alpha)(x + \beta)$, where α and β are positive numbers.

Pause and reflect now. That is just a fancy way of saying stop and think. Write a journal entry and say how you feel about factorising. You also need to make some clear notes about how to factorise expressions.

Quadratics of the form $x^2 - bx + c$

Notice the difference here. Both signs were positive in the quadratic form above – here one sign is negative and that does change what we do. Now we have to look at the sign of each term very carefully.

Example 1

Let's factorise $x^2 - 11x + 30$ so that it comes out in the form $(x +/- ?)(x +/- ?)$

- First of all check the coefficient of x^2 – in this case it is 1 so that's OK so far.
- Look at the constant term – we need to find two numbers that multiply together to give +30.

    Possible combinations include

    +10 and +3,   + 15 and +2,   +1and +30,   +5 and +6

But there is a problem – we need to have a negative coefficient of x and none of these combinations will give us a negative $11x$. So we need to consider negative factors. The best way to tackle this is to consider two factors that multiply to give the constant but add to give the coefficient of x.

Think about this for a moment
– what two numbers will multiply to +30 and add to –11?

This implies that both must be negative (remember, a negative multiplied by a negative gives a positive; and a larger negative added to a smaller negative gives a negative).

The factors must be –6 and –5.

So the factorisation is

$$x^2 - 11x + 30 = (x - 6)(x - 5)$$

Look at how the quadratic has factorised. The –6 in the first bracket and the x in the second bracket have been multiplied together to give –6x and the –5 and the other x have multiplied together to give –5x. In the same way the –6 and –5 have multiplied to generate the +30.

Check: expand the brackets on the right-hand side and you should get the left-hand side.

(Don't forget to tidy up the quadratic by adding the two middle terms.)

Example 2
Factorise $a^2 - 5a + 6$.

Here we want factors of +6 that add up to –5. The first step is to check the coefficient of a.

Just a reminder, the coefficient is the number in front of the variable (shown by a letter), so in this example it is -5 because the term is -5a

This is 1 so we can confidently say that it will factorise in the form
$$a^2 - 5a + 6 = (a +/- \ ?)(a +/- \ ?)$$

Now we list the possible factors that we can use here.
Since we need to generate +6 as the constant term we know that the factors must both be either positive numbers or negative numbers.

The possibilities are:
–1 and –6, or
+1 and +6, or
–2 and –3, or
+2 and +3.

We also need them to add to the coefficient of x, and that is –5.

This means the factors we need must be –2 and –3.

So the factorisation is
$$a^2 - 5a + 6 = (a - 2)(a - 3)$$

Don't forget to check this solution.

Quadratics with a negative constant term
This section refers to quadratics of the form

$$x^2 + bx - c \qquad \text{and} \qquad x^2 - bx - c$$

In other words quadratic expressions in which the constant term is negative and the coefficient of x may be positive or negative.

Example 1
Factorise $x^2 + x - 12$.
A factorisation of the form $(x + ?)\,(x + ?)$ will give an x^2 term with a coefficient of 1 but the constant term is –12 and that suggests that one of the missing numbers must be positive and one must be negative.

Therefore we are looking for factors of –12 that add to +1.

Think about this for a moment. remember the running theme in this book is first to convince yourself and then to convince another person.

Now write down all of the factors of -12, and do make sure you have them all. Now look for the factors that add up to +1 and write them down.

Back to the factorisation.

The factors of –12 are

–1 and +12,   +1 and –12,   +3 and –4,   –3 and +4.

We also need them to add to +1; so that means that we must use –3 and +4. So, the factorisation is

$$x^2 + x - 12 = (x - 3)(x + 4)$$

Don't forget to do the check.

Example 2

Factorise $x^2 - x - 6$

The numerical value of the coefficient of x^2 is 1 and so we can aim for the form

$$(x +/- ?) (x +/- ?).$$

The constant term is –6 and the coefficient of x is –1, so we need to find factors of –6 that add up to –1.

This means that the factors must be –3 and +2. (You have to have a + and a - to generate that -6)

Therefore

$$x^2 - x - 6 = (x + 2)(x - 3)$$

Again you need to convince yourself and then convince another person. Expand the brackets on the right-hand side and that should give you the expression on the left-hand side.

Exercise 6.8

Factorise these quadratic expressions.

1    $x^2 - x - 2$ 2 $x^2 - x - 12$

3    $x^2 + 2x - 15$ 4 $x^2 + 7x + 12$

5    $x^2 + 5x - 14$ 6 $x^2 + 2x - 35$

7    $x^2 + 7x - 18$ 8 $x^2 - 16$

9    $x^2 + 11x - 12$ 10 $x^2 + x - 90$

Changing the Subject

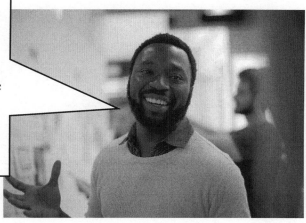

This operation is also known as transposition of formulae or transformation of formulae. By changing the subject, we mean rearranging the equation to make any one of the variable (letters) appear on its own on one side of the equation by making sure that everything else is moved to the other side of the equal sign. To do this, you use exactly the same rules as when solving equations – this means that you have the skills already.

Making x the Subject

This means that we want to get x on its own on one side of the equation. So, for example, starting with, if we want x to be the subject, we need to get the x term on its own and everything else on the other side of the equal sign.

Example 1

Starting with $f = y + 3x$, the first thing to do is to take y from both sides

$$f - y = y + 3x - y$$

The y's on the right-hand side cancel each other out, so the next line looks like this

$$f - y = 3x$$

Now we need to undo the 3 times x on the right-hand side – this means by dividing both sides by 3

Now the 3's on the right-hand side cancel leaving

$$\frac{f - y}{3} = \frac{3x}{3}$$

Now we are rewriting this to show the x on the left hand side of the equation and everything else on the right hand side.

$$x = \frac{f - y}{3}$$

Example 2

Let's look at example involving brackets.
We want to make x the subject in this equation

$$v(x+v)=y^2$$

First, expand the brackets

$$vx+v^2=y^2$$

Now subtract v^2 from both sides

$$vx+v^2-v^2=y^2-v^2$$

$$vx=y^2-v^2$$

Now look at the left-hand side – this is a product, it is $v \times x$, so to make x the subject we undo this by dividing both sides by v.

This gives

$$\frac{\cancel{v}x}{\cancel{v}}=\frac{y^2-v^2}{v}$$

$$x=\frac{y^2-v^2}{v}$$

because the v's on the left-hand side cancel.

Dealing with fractions

A fraction is a quotient – in other words, one quantity is divided by another.
So we can undo it by multiplying, in just the same way as you did with equations.

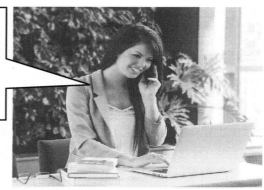

Wow, 'quotient' what does this mean? Quotient just means a division, so the numerator (top) of a fraction is divided by the denominator, (bottom) of the fraction, cool huh!

O.K let's move on and have a look at another example, but you need to have a go at it first before looking at our answer. Remember the only way to learn maths is to do maths, it really is important for you.

Have a go at making m the subject in this equation

$$\frac{m}{p} = y$$

It really is important for you to have a go first and then look at our solution.
There are a few hints at the bottom of the page but do try your own solution first and then you will have something to reflect on, that is how we all learn.

Hints

if we want to make m the subject we need to undo the division in this fraction.

To do this you multiply both sides by whatever is in the denominator of the fraction, in this case p.

Have a go at this now, multiply both sides by p and don't forget to cancel on the left-hand side. Have a go at this before you look at our solution.

$$\frac{m}{p} = y$$

Multiply both sides by p This will eliminate the fraction.

$$p \times \frac{m}{p} = p \times y$$

More correctly in algebra we do not use a x to show multiplication. When we multiply in algebra, we put the variables, shown here as letters, next to each other so

$$p \times m \text{ is } pm$$

so we have

$$\frac{pm}{p} = py$$

Now the p's on the left hand side cancel

$$\frac{\cancel{p}m}{\cancel{p}} = py$$

$$m = py$$

Just to be clear, we are not just crossing out the p values, we are saying p divided by p = 1 and then one times m is m so that is the reason why the p's can be cancelled.

Dealing with Square Roots

A square root is often in the denominator of a fraction.
For example,

$$y = \frac{p}{\sqrt{x}}$$

This can look a bit scary but don't panic.

To make x the subject of this expression, remember that you can look to eliminating the fraction by multiplying both sides by a certain term. In this example, multiply both sides by $\sqrt{x}$

This will mean that the $\sqrt{x}$ term will cancel on the right-hand side

$$\sqrt{x}\, y = \frac{\cancel{\sqrt{x}}\, p}{\cancel{\sqrt{x}}}$$

So now we have $\qquad \sqrt{x}y = p$

This is better, but we want x on its own on one side of the equation and everything else on the other side.

$$\frac{\sqrt{x\cancel{y}}}{\cancel{x}} = \frac{p}{y}$$

Look at the left-hand side of the equation. There are two terms side by side – in algebra this means a product – so these two terms are multiplied together. If they are multiplied they can be divided and that is what we need to do next.

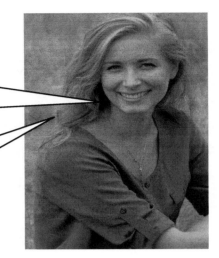

We want x on its own and the closest we have is $\sqrt{x}$ so therefore we divide both sides by y and this will leave the $\sqrt{x}$ on its own.

This is because the y's on the left hand side cancel out.

$$\sqrt{x} = \frac{p}{y}$$

Now we are close to what we want – but we want x rather than $\sqrt{x}$

How do we get from $\sqrt{x}$ to x ?

The simple answer is to square it because $\sqrt{x} \times \sqrt{x}$

But we must do the same thing to both sides of the equation so

$$(\sqrt{x})^2 = \left(\frac{p}{y}\right)^2$$

$$x = \left(\frac{p}{y}\right)^2$$

Example 2
Make x the subject of

$$v = \frac{m}{\sqrt{x}}$$

Multiply both sides by $\sqrt{x}$ to eliminate the fraction.

This gives

$$\sqrt{x}\, v = \frac{\sqrt{x}\, m}{\sqrt{x}}$$

Cancel the $\sqrt{x}$ on the right-hand side to give

$$\sqrt{x}\, v = m$$

Again we have a product on the left-hand side, so to isolate the $\sqrt{x}$ we divide both sides by v

$$\frac{\sqrt{x}\,\cancel{v}}{\cancel{v}} = \frac{m}{v}$$

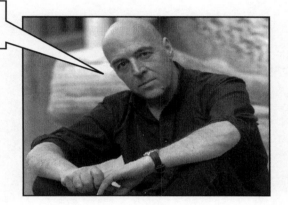

Remember 'product' means they are multiplied, so to 'undo' it we divide

The v's on the left-hand side cancel leaving

$$\sqrt{x} = \frac{m}{v}$$

Now square both sides

$$\sqrt{x}^2 = \left(\frac{m}{v}\right)^2$$

$$x = \left(\frac{m}{v}\right)^2$$

Example 3

Here is an example involve negative terms.

We want to make x the subject of

$$h = m - \frac{1}{\sqrt{x}}$$

All we do is 'undo' this in stages as before. First subtract m from both sides

$$h - m = m - \frac{1}{\sqrt{x}} - m$$

This gives

$$h - m = -\frac{1}{\sqrt{x}}$$

Remember if you have a square root and square it, you get the number that you square rooted.
So $\sqrt{3}^2 = \sqrt{3} \times \sqrt{3}$
$= 3$
It is the same with $\sqrt{x}$

$\sqrt{x}^2 = \sqrt{x} \times \sqrt{x}$ (or $x^{1/2} \times x^{1/2}$)
$= x$

Now we can use a technique described earlier –
multiplying throughout by −1.

This is a lot easier to deal with, we have already seen
equations in this format.

$$- h + m = \frac{1}{\sqrt{x}}$$

which we can rewrite as

$$h - m = \frac{1}{\sqrt{x}}$$

Multiply both sides by √x to eliminate the √x on the right-hand side to leave 1 on its
own

$$\sqrt{x}\,(h - m) = \frac{\cancel{\sqrt{x}}.1}{\cancel{\sqrt{x}}}$$

on the right hand
side the dot is a
correct mathema-
tial way of saying
multiply

Notice here we have cancelled the √x on the right
hand side and that just leaves the 1. But what does
that leave us on the left hand side ?

we can divide both sides by (*h-m*) and that
will leave us with the √x on the left-hand side to deal with as the next stage.

$$\frac{\sqrt{x}\,\cancel{(h - m)}}{\cancel{(h-m)}} = \frac{1}{(h-m)}$$

Now we need to sort out the left hand side. Look at it, it is two terms multiplied, we call this a product. So we need to divide by the one we do not want it be left on the left hand side.

So we cancel the ($h - m$) on the left hand side as shown above, now w eneed to eliminate the square root

Now we need to square both sides, to eliminate the square root.

$$\sqrt{x} = \frac{1}{(h-m)}$$

$$x = \left(\frac{1}{(h-m)}\right)^2$$

Remember when you square a square root you get back to the number that was square rooted. So $\sqrt{3}^2 = \sqrt{3} \times \sqrt{3} = 3$
it is the same in algebra, $\sqrt{x}^2 = x$

So we needed to square both sides and that eliminated the $\sqrt{x}$ on the left hand side.

Example 4

Make x the subject of $bx^2 - h = y^2$

undo the h by adding h to both sides

$$bx^2 - h + h = y^2 + h$$

$$bx^2 = y^2 + h$$

now undo the product on the left hand side (bx^2) by dividing both sides by b

$$\frac{bx^2}{b} = \frac{y^2 + h}{b}$$

Now the b's on the left hand side cancel out

$$x^2 = \frac{y^2 + h}{b}$$

Now take the square root for both sides, this will give us x on the left hand side.

$$x = \sqrt{\left(\frac{y^2 + h}{b}\right)}$$

Exercise 6.9
Make x the subject of these equations.

1    $x + y = a + b$

2    $xv - l = k$

3    $hj - x = b$

4    $\dfrac{n(b - v)}{x} = y$

5    $n(b - x) = h + d$

6    $dx^2 - k = g^2$

7    $f(a + x) = y$

8    $\dfrac{m(x + d)}{a} = h$

9    $d(a + 9x) = y$

10    $mx + y = c$

How to deal with Algebraic Fractions

$\dfrac{5x^3}{8x}$ and $\dfrac{8(x + 9)}{2x}$ are examples of algebraic fractions.

As we have already seen, fractions can be simplified by cancelling when, and only when, there is a common factor in the numerator and denominator.

In your journal explain what is meant by a common factor? Remember the recurrent theme of this book – convince yourself and then convince another person.

Look at this operation to get the feel for common factors. It is written it out in rather a long winded way so that you can see what is going on. With practice you will be able to do problems like this in one step.

$$\frac{4x^4}{12x} = \frac{4 \times x \, x \, x \, x \, x \, x \, x}{12 \times x \, x}$$

$$= \frac{x \, x \, x \, x \, x \, x}{3 \, x}$$

$$= \frac{x \, x \, x \, x}{3}$$

$$= \frac{x^3}{3}$$

You do need to think a bit here.

Cancel the 4 in the numerator (top) with the 12 in the denominator (bottom), so $^4/_{12}$ becomes $^1/_3$.

Remember it is algebra so we do NOT write $1x$, it is just x

Example 1

Simplify $\dfrac{9(x+4)}{3x}$

First, look for common factors. Obviously 9 and 3 will cancel because they have common factors, so

$$\frac{9(x+4)}{3x} = \frac{3(x+4)}{x}$$

$$= \frac{3x+12}{x} \qquad \text{Expand the bracket in the numerator}$$

remember the x in the denominator is a common denominator

$$= \frac{3x}{x} + \frac{12}{x}$$

$$= 3 + \frac{12}{x}$$

In your journal make notes about what we have done here. On the left-hand side of the page note down this example, and preferably one of your own as well. On the right-hand side of the page, describe the steps in the method for simplifying these types of questions.

Multiplying Algebraic Fractions

When multiplying algebraic fractions, look for and cancel any factor that is common to both the numerator and the denominator. Then, when it is not possible to cancel any further, multiply the remaining numerators and denominators.

For example, suppose we want to simplify

$$\frac{x^8}{y^2} \times \frac{x^4 y}{z} \times \frac{z^6}{x^3}$$

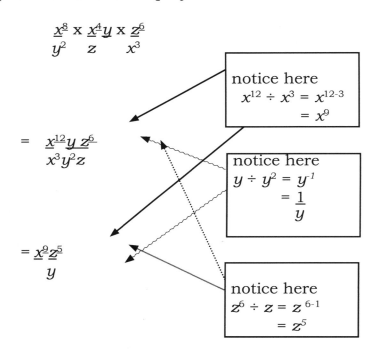

notice here
$$x^{12} \div x^3 = x^{12-3}$$
$$= x^9$$

$$= \frac{x^{12} y \, z^6}{x^3 y^2 z}$$

notice here
$$y \div y^2 = y^1$$
$$= \frac{1}{y}$$

$$= \frac{x^9 z^5}{y}$$

notice here
$$z^6 \div z = z^{6-1}$$
$$= z^5$$

Dividing Algebraic Fractions

$5 \div {}^1/_3$ means 'how many thirds are there in 5?'

When you divide something by an algebraic fraction, it is the same as multiplying it by its reciprocal. Look what happens when we do it with numbers.

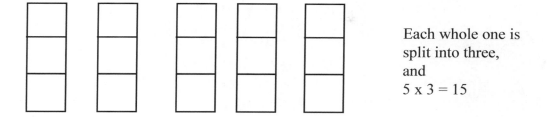

Each whole one is
split into three,
and
5 x 3 = 15

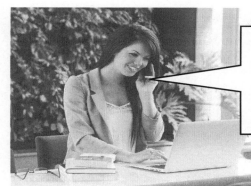

Clearly there are 15 thirds in 5, so $5 \div \frac{1}{3} = 15$

But the reciprocal of $\frac{1}{3}$ is 3, so since 5 × 3 = 15 we could have got the same answer by multiplying by the reciprocal.

Reciprocals

The reciprocal of any number is the number that you multiply it by to get an answer of 1. The reciprocal of 3 is $\frac{1}{3}$.   The reciprocal of is $\frac{1}{25}$ is 25.

The reciprocal of $\frac{2}{33}$ is $\frac{33}{2}$

So when you are dividing by a fraction, it has the same result as multiplying by the reciprocal of the fraction. It is easy to get the reciprocal of a fraction – just invert it

Adding and Subtracting Algebraic Fractions

When you are dealing with fractions written in number form, you cannot add or subtract the fractions unless they have a common denominator. The same is true for algebraic fractions.

Example 1

Simplify $\dfrac{4x + 1}{3} + \dfrac{3x - 2}{2}$

The denominators are 2 and 3, so the lowest common denominator is the lowest common multiple (LCM) of the denominators of the fractions – in this case 6.

So we need to multiply the first fraction (above and below) by 2 and the second fraction by 3.

So

$$\frac{4x + 1}{3} + \frac{3x - 2}{2} = \frac{6(4x + 1)}{3} + \frac{6(3x - 2)}{2}$$

$$= 2(4x + 1) + 3(3x - 2)$$

$$= 8x + 1 + 9x - 6$$

$$= 17x - 4$$

Remember, convince yourself, then convince another person.

Example 2

$$\frac{6x - 3}{4} - \frac{x + 7}{2} = \frac{6x - 3}{4} - \frac{2(x + 7)}{2}$$

multiply by 4 to get rid of the fraction

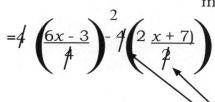

the 4's in the first term cancel
the 4 and the 2 in the second term also cancel

$$= 6x - 3 - 2(2x + 7)$$

Now expand the second bracket

$$= 6x - 3 - 4x - 28$$

Now collect like terms

$$= 2x - 31$$

Now is a good time to pause and reflect on what we have done.
Rewrite this calculation in your journal down the left hand side and make red pen notes down the right hand side.

Sequences

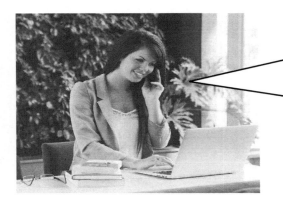

In an arithmetic sequence the term in the sequence increases or decreases by a fixed number, in other words the same amount. This number is called the common difference. The first term in the sequece is called u, the next term u_2, the next u_3 and so the nth term is u_n.

Look at this sequence.

$$\_\_, 8, 11, 14, 17, 20, 23, \_\_$$

It is quite easy to work out the first and last terms in the sequence by working out the common difference. The sequence goes up in 3's.

$$\_\_, 8, 11, 14, 17, 20, 23, \_\_$$
$$+3 \quad +3 \quad +3 \quad +3 \quad +3$$

This means it is quite easy to work out the missing terms, they must be 5 and 26

The skill is now to get an algebraic equation to describe the sequence.

Term	Value	1st differences
1	5	
2	8	3
3	11	3
4	14	3
5	17	3
6	20	3
7	23	3
8	26	3

Notice, here in the table, the values go up in 3's. So if when you work out 3 x 1st term that is 3 BUT there is 5 in the table so you have to add on 2.

$(3 \times 1) + 2 = 5$

Does this work for all of the other values in the table?

You should have found that this does work for all of the other values in the table.

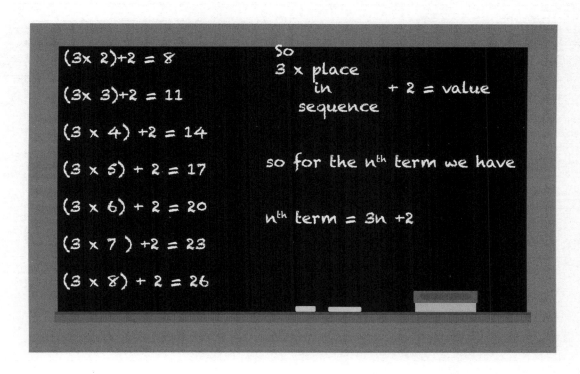

$(3 \times 2) + 2 = 8$

$(3 \times 3) + 2 = 11$

$(3 \times 4) + 2 = 14$

$(3 \times 5) + 2 = 17$

$(3 \times 6) + 2 = 20$

$(3 \times 7) + 2 = 23$

$(3 \times 8) + 2 = 26$

So
$3 \times$ place in sequence $+ 2 =$ value

so for the nth term we have

n^{th} term $= 3n + 2$

Ex 6.2

1 Write each of the following sequences and then select the correct expression for the nth term from the list.

a) 15, 30, 45, 60

b) 6, 12, 18, 24, 30

c) 4, 5, 6, 7, 8

d) 3, 5, 7, 9, 11

e) 2, 5, 8, 11

f) 2, 8, 14, 20

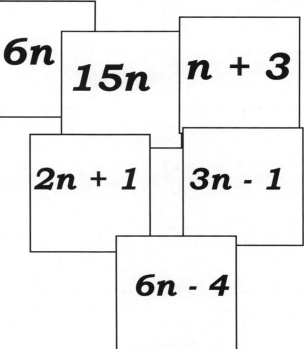

$6n$

$15n$

$n + 3$

$2n + 1$

$3n - 1$

$6n - 4$

2   Copy and complete the mapping diagrams

a)

Term number (n)	3n	term
1 ⟶	3 ⟶	7
2 ⟶	6 ⟶	10
3 ⟶	9 ⟶	13
4 ⟶	..... ⟶	.....
10 ⟶	...... ⟶	.....
n ⟶	.... ⟶	_____

b)

Term number (n)	5n	term
1 ⟶	5 ⟶	6
2 ⟶	10 ⟶	11
3 ⟶	15 ⟶	16
4 ⟶	20 ⟶	21
20 ⟶	.... ⟶	.....
n ⟶	.... ⟶	.....

3   Here are the first five terms of a sequence

7. 11, 15, 19, 23

The sequence follows the rules add 4 so write this in columns

n	$4n$	Term
1	4	7
2	8	11
3	12	?
4	16	?
5	?	

a)   Draw a mapping diagram as you did in Q2.

b)   (i) Write down the 10th term

(ii) Write down the nth term.

4   Here are three sequences, find the nth term

a   2   4   6   8   10

b   1   5   9   13   17

c   4   12   20   28   ?

5 Here are 2 more harder sequences.
Copy and complete the mapping diagram

a)

Term Number (n)		Term
1	1 x 2	3
2	2 x 3	8
3	3 x 4	15
4	4 x 5	24
5	5 x 6	35
n	....	....

b)

Term Number (n)		Term
1	1 x 4	7
2	2 x 5	16
3	3 x 6	27
5	4 x 7	55
6	6 x 8	72
n	....	......

Tutorial Progress questions Expand these expressions.

1 $(x + 5)(x + 2) =$ **2** $(x + 3)(x + 7) =$

3 $(y + 2)(y + 4) =$ **4** $(x - 4)(x + 5) =$

5 $(2x + 2)(x - 4) =$ **6** $(3x + 5)(x - 2) =$

7 $(3d - 5)(4d - 7) =$ **8** $(3f - 8)(4f + 2) =$

9 $(7g - 4)(g - 3) =$ **10** $(x + 7)^2 =$

11 $(f + 3)^2 =$ **12** $(x - 8)^2 =$

13 $(d + 2)^2 =$

Simplify the following.

14 $\dfrac{x^4 y^3}{z^5} \times \dfrac{xyz}{x^3}$ **15** $\dfrac{18pb^2}{6pb}$

7 Solving Simultaneous Equations
One-Minute Overview
Simultaneous equations are two or more equations that have to be solved at the same time, that is why they are called simultaneous, simultaneous means 'at the same time'.

In this chapter you will learn to solve simultaneous equations with two unknowns by using the:
- Elimination method;
- Substitution method.

You can only solve an equation when there is one unknown.
So an equation like $2x + 2y = 18$ is not solvable. Think about what happens in real life – if you have two mystery whole numbers that add to 10 they could be 1 and 9, or 2 and 8, or 3 and 7, or 4 and 6, or 5 and 5.

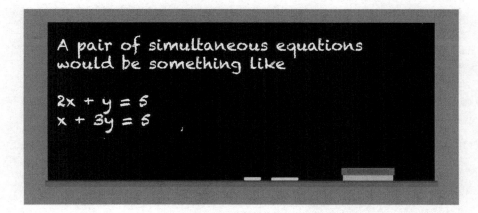

A pair of simultaneous equations would be something like

$2x + y = 5$
$x + 3y = 5$

At this stage we do not know the values of x and y (unless you have guessed). But the point to understand here is that the value of x is the same in both equations. Similarly the value of y is also the same. This allows us to use one of two methods to solve these equations – either:
- elimination or
- substitution.

The Elimination Method

There are some words you need to know. In algebra we use letters. These letters can vary in value. This means they have a special name, they are called variables. The number in front of a variable (letter) is the coefficient of that variable. So in $2x$, 2 is the coefficient, in $5m$, 5 is the coefficient.

The idea here is to remove one of the variables. This will leave us with just one unknown.

Let's look at an example.

$$a + b = 7 \quad \text{.............. (equation 1)}$$

$$2a + b = 10 \quad \text{...............(equation 2)}$$

We cannot solve these equations because there are more than one variable. But we do have one vital piece of information. Whatever the valued for a and b in these equations are, they are the same foir both equations.

Here it is again

$$a + b = 7 \quad \dots\dots\dots\dots \text{(equation 1)}$$

$$2a + b = 10 \quad \dots\dots\dots\dots\text{(equation 2)}$$

we need to consider the coefficients of a and b. Can we eliminate either the a's or the b's ?

Look at what happens if we work out (equation 2 – equation 1)

$a + b = 7 \quad \dots\dots\dots\dots \text{(equation 1)}$

$2a + b = 10 \quad \dots\dots\dots\dots\text{(equation 2)}$

$2a - a = a \qquad\qquad b - b = 0 \qquad\qquad 10 - 7 = 3$

The b's are eliminated – there aren't any left.

So we are left with $a = 3$.

The next step is to substitute for a in one of the equations – equation 1 would be the simplest to use.

Equation 1 is $\hspace{8cm} a + b = 7$

Since we know that $a = 3$, then we can say that $\hspace{3.5cm} 3 + b = 7$

which means that: $\hspace{7cm} b = 4$

Check:

substitute for a and b into equation 2 (the one we didn't use in the substitution of a). This gives $(2 \times 3) + 4 = 10$, just as it should. So we know we are correct.

Example 2

$$2x + y = 9 \qquad \text{(equation 1)}$$

$$x - y = 3 \qquad \text{(equation 2)}$$

Look at the coefficients – for the y's are + and – so if we add them we can eliminate the y's.

So $3x = 12$.

We must now is solve for x.

Dividing both sides by 3 gives

$$\frac{\cancel{3}x}{\cancel{3}} = \frac{12}{3}$$

so $\quad x = 4$

The next step is to substitute for x into one of the original equations, say equation 1.

$$(2 \times 4) + y = 9$$

$$8 + y = 9$$

therefore $y = 1 \quad (8 + 1 = 9)$

Check: putting $x = 4$ and y into equation 2 we get

$$4 - 1 = 3 \qquad \text{and so it must be correct.}$$

Exercise 7.1

Solve these simultaneous equations by using the elimination method.

1 $2x + y = 10$
         $x + y = 7$

2 $x + y = 8$
         $2x + y = 13$

3 $3x + y = 7$
         $x + y = 3$

4 $3x + y = 31$
         $2x + y = 24$

5 $x + y = 3$
         $3x + y = 7$

6 $2a + b = 20$
         $a + b = 15$

7 $a - b = 6$
         $a + b = 12$

8 $a + 4b = 25$
         $a + b = 7$

9 $2x = y + 5$
         $4x = y + 13$

10 $3m - n = 5$
         $m + n = 11$

A good study tip is to work with a studymate and explain a solution to that person.
If s/he doesn't understand then it is probably the quality of your explanation that needs to improve.

Don't insult the other person's intelligence.

The Substitution Method

This is the second method of solving simultaneous equations. In this method we change one of the equations and then put that changed equation back into other equation. Remember you can only solve an equation if there is one unknown.

Example 1

$$x + y = 5$$

$$2x + y = 9$$

The first step is to rearrange equation 2 to make y the subject.
So equation 2 becomes

$$y = 9 - 2x$$

Now here is the new bit – we substitute this into equation 1 take out y and put 9 - 2x in its place.

So this now reads

$$x + (9 - 2x) = 5$$

Now let's tidy up $\qquad\qquad\qquad\qquad\qquad$ (x - 2x = -x)

$$-x + 9 = 5$$

We can rewrite this as

$$9 - x = 5$$

$$9 - x + x = 5 + x$$

$$9 = 5 + x$$

$$9 - 5 = 5 + x - 5$$

$$4 = x \quad \text{or } x = 4$$

Now we have found the value of x, we can substitute for x into equation 1 to find the value of y.

$$4 + y = 5$$

Check: putting $x = 4$ and $y = 1$ in equation 2 gives

$$8 + 1 = 9 \text{ so you know you are correct.}$$

Example 2

$$3a - 2b = 0 \qquad \text{(equation 1)}$$

$$2a + b = 7 \qquad \text{(equation 2)}$$

Here we are going to rearrange equation 2 to make b the subject.
To do this we need to take $2a$
from both sides giving

Note that all we have done here is to take out the b and replace it with 7 - 2a

$$b = 7 - 2a$$

Now we substitute for b into equation 1

$$3a - 2(7 - 2a) = 0$$

This gives an equation with only a as the variable.

$$3a - 2(7 - 2a) = 0$$

$$3a - 14 + 4a = 0$$

$$7a - 14 = 0$$

$$a = 2$$

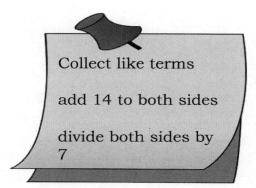

Collect like terms

add 14 to both sides

divide both sides by 7

Now substitute for a into equation 1.

$$3a - 2b = 0$$

$$6 - 2b = 0$$

$$6 - 2b + 2b = 0 + 2b$$

$$6 = 2b$$

$$b = 3$$

add 2b to both sides

divide both sides by 2

So $a = 2$ and $b = 3$

Check: substitute for a and b into equation 2 giving

$$(2 \times 2) + 3 = 7 \text{ so it is correct}$$

An Extra Skill

Look at this
If 4 + 3 = 7 and we multiply every term by 2 then we get 8 + 6 = 14. This shows that if you multiply everything in an equation by the same number, the equality is still true.
Try multiplying everything by 3, you get 12 + 9 = 21.
Try some more for yourself and convince yourself that this is always true, then convince another person.

There is one more area to be aware of – and that is where you have to multiply an equation throughout.

Example 3

$$2y + 5z = 24 \quad \text{(equation 1)}$$

$$4y + 3z = 20 \quad \text{(equation 2)}$$

Bck to our simultaneous equations

$$2y + 5z = 24 \quad \text{(equation 1)}$$

$$4y + 3z = 20. \text{ (equation 2)}$$

Look at the coefficients of y and z. There is absolutely no point in adding or subtracting these equations – it will not eliminate either of the variables. But there is another way of dealing with the equations – look at equation 1.

If we double everything in equation 1, look at what happens

$$4y + 10z = 48 \qquad \text{(equation 3)}$$

We have generated a new equation to put with equation 2.
$$4y + 10z = 48$$

$$4y + 3z = 20.$$

Now we have two coefficients that are the same so we can eliminate the y's and then carry on as before. You try it now.

You should get $y = 2$ and $z = 4$.

Exercise 7.2

Solve the following simultaneous equations.

1      $a + b = 9$
         $2a - 3b = 8$

2      $a + 2b = 8$
         $2a + 3b = 13$

3      $2m + n = 17$
         $5m + 2n = 40$

4      $2x + 2y = 10$
         $x + 2y = 8$

5      $5r + 2s = 44$
         $2r - s = 5$

6      $6x + 2y = 50$
         $3x + 2y = 29$

7      $a + 2b = 25$
         $2a + b = 35$

8      $m + n = 9$
         $3m + 5n = 41$

9      $2a + 3b = 63$
         $2a + b = 37$

10     $x - y = -1$
         $2x - y = 0$

Problems solved by Simultaneous Equations

There are some real problems that we can solve using simultaneous equations. They are the type of problem where we need to establish two equations.

Find two numbers whose sum is 18 and difference is 12.

Let's call the numbers x and y.

$$x + y = 18 \qquad \text{(equation 1)}$$

$$x - y = 12 \qquad \text{(equation 2)}$$

Look at the coefficients of y, there is a $+1$ and a -1 so adding will eliminate them. So adding equations 1 and 2

$$x + x = 2x$$

$$y + (-y) = 0$$

$$18 + 12 = 30$$

$$\text{So } 2x = 30$$

$$x = 15$$

Now we substitute for x into equation 1 getting
$$15 + y = 18$$
$$\text{so } y = 3$$

Don't forget the check.

Exercise 7.3

1   Find two numbers with a sum of 12 and a difference of 4.

2   Twice one number added to three times another number gives 41. One lot of the first number added to one lot of the second number is sixteen. Find both numbers.

3   Three times one number plus twice another number gives 22. When one lot of each number is added together the answer is 9. What are the numbers?

4   Twice one number plus three times another number gives twenty-six. When one lot of each of the numbers are added together the answer is 10. What are the numbers?

5   Three litres of water and two chocolate bars cost £1. 15. Two litres of water and three chocolate bars costs £1.10. Find the cost of one litre of water and of one chocolate bar.

6   Three adult fares and one child fare on a bus costs £2.40. Four adults and two children on the same trip costs £3.40. Find the cost for one adult and for one child for this trip.

7   Two adult train fares and two child train fares for a particular journey cost £60.80. One adult and three children costs £50.40. Find the cost for one adult.

8   In a furniture store three chairs and two stools cost £290. Four of the same chairs and three of the same stools costs £395. Find the cost of one chair and of one stool.

9   Five sodas and three ice creams cost £5.25 whereas one soda and one ice cream cost £1.25. Find the cost of an ice cream.

10   A baseball cap and a mobile phone cost £26.49 but two baseball caps and three phones cost £72.97. Find the cost of a phone

Tutorial

Progress Questions

1. $2x + y = 16$
       $x + y = 9$

2. $x + y = 9$
     $2x + y = 14$

3. $3x + y = 10$
       $x + y = 4$

4. $3x + y = 41$
     $2x + y = 29$

5. $x + y = 3$
    $3x + 2y = 8$

6. Find two numbers with a sum of 9 and a difference of 5.

7. Twice one number added to three times another number gives 66. One lot of the first number added to one lot of the second number gives twenty-seven. Find both numbers.

8. Three times one number plus twice another number gives 39. When one lot of each number is added together the answer is 17. What are the numbers?

9. Twice one number plus three times another number adds to twenty-nine. When one lot of each of the numbers are added together the answer is 13. What are the numbers?

10. Three adult fares and one child fare on a bus costs £3.15. Four adults and two children on the same trip costs £4.50. Find the cost of one adult and one child for this trip.

Discussion

Make a journal entry on the techniques used in this chapter. Discuss the problem-solving techniques with another person – please remember the theme of this book, first of all convince yourself then convince another person.

Time for a journal entry.
Write down how you feel about algebra now.
Look back at the work you have done in this book and ask yourself ' do I feel any different?'

Reflection in a mirror showsx us what we look like at that moment.

Personal reflection means thinking about how well we are doing and what we need to look at next. People at work often work through a SWOT analysis.

S strengths: What am I good at, what do I do well?

W weaknesses: What are my weaknesses and how can I improve my performance?

O opportunities: What opportunities are there for me to improve?

T threats: What threats exist to damage my future performance?

8 Graphs and Algebra

One-Minute Overview
Graphs can be used to illustrate algebraic expressions.

In this chapter you will learn about:
*   Straight line graphs and their equations;
*   Graphs of simultaneous linear equations;
*   Graphs of quadratics and cubics.

Straight Line Graphs

Here is an equation which generates an easy graph to get started with, $y = x + 1$. The first step is to make a table of values. To do this we allocate values to the variable x and work out what the corresponding values of y are.

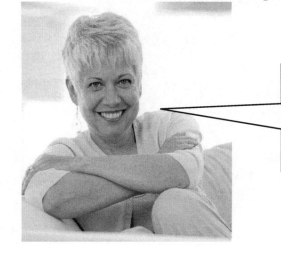

This means we need to form a table of values. Here we have simply said let x be 1, so since the equation is $y = x + 1$, we substitute 1 for x, so when x is 1, y must be 2. So now let $x = 2$, so y will equal 2 + 1 = 3 and so on.

x	1	2	3
y	2	3	4

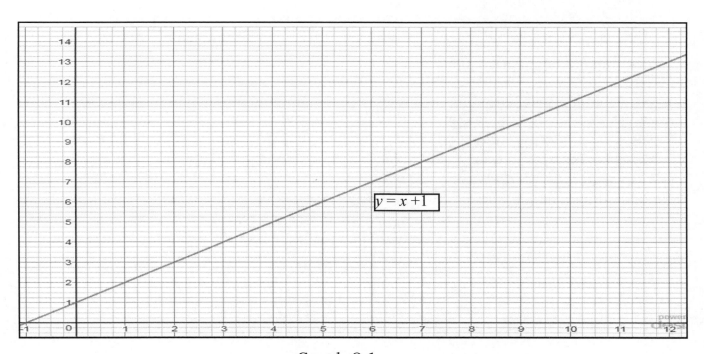

$y = x + 1$

Graph 8.1

So the points to be plotted are (1, 2), (2, 3) and (3, 4) where the numbers indicates the (x, y) points on the graph

Notice we have only worked out three points. You can draw a straight line with just two points but the third is recommended for accuracy. So we have a graph that shows the equation of $y = x + 1$.

Now is a good time to make a note in your journal. It is a good idea right now to write down how we created the last graph. Draw the graph on the left hand side of your page and write notes in red on the right hand side. These notes will help you to learn.

Look at the line on the graph. Choose a number on the x-axis (the horizontal one) and move up (or down) to the y-axis (the vertical one) – what do you notice?

You should have noticed that at any point on the graph, the y-value is always one more than the x-value. Are you surprised by this? Think about the equation of the graph, $y = x + 1$.

This equation tells us that whatever value of x you use, y will always be one more than it. This means that the equation of the line is the general rule that applies to every point on the line.

Let's look at another graph, $y = x + 2$. First we compose a table of values.

x	-2	-1	0	1
y	0	1	2	3

Now we can draw the graph.
The points we plot are $(x, y) = (-2, 0), (-1, 1), (0, 2), (1, 3)$.

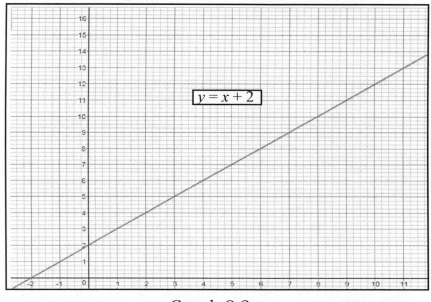

Graph 8.2

Look carefully at graph 8.2 and compare it with the graph of $y = x + 1$, what do you notice?
You should see that it is the same graph but it is shifted one up on the y - axis.
In case you have problems seeing that, we have put them together in graph 8.3.

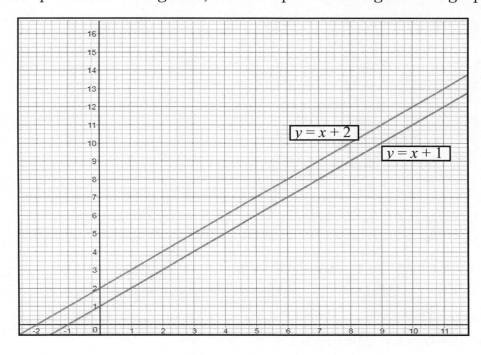

Graph 8.3

And so we can go on. In graph 8.4 we have added the line for $y = x$

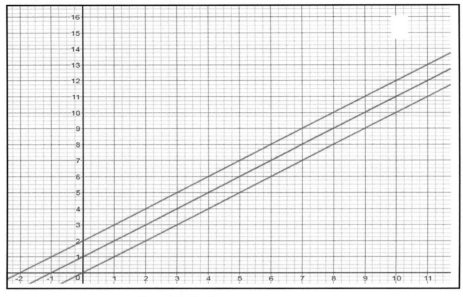

Graph 8.4

In graph 8.5 we have added $y = x - 1$.

Graph 8.5

You can see that:
- all these graphs are straight lines;
- all have the same slope – and are therefore the lines are parallel.

How Do We Work Out the Slope of a Line?

The slope of a graph is called its gradient. The gradient is the 'drop divided by the step', in other words the distance along the *y*-axis divided by the distance across the *x*-axis.

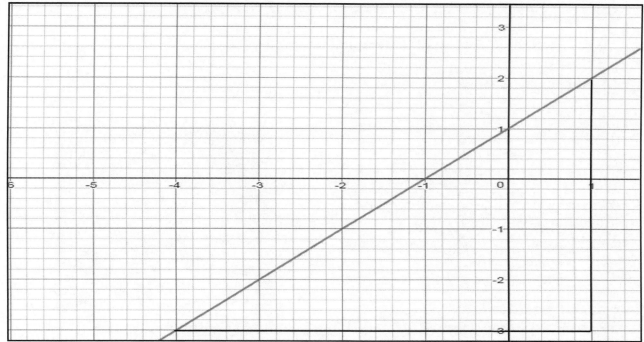

Graph 8.6

In graph 8.6 we have illustrated the 'drop' and the 'step' to make it clear what we mean. Mathematically, a drop is the difference between two *y*-values. In the graph in this example you calculate the drop shown with 2 – (–3); this gives 15.

Now do the same with the step shown here. This is the difference in the *x*-values. You should find that this also comes to 5 for this graph. (If you are not sure about these calculations, then simply count the squares.)

The gradient is called *m*. So in this graph of *y* = *x* +1

$$m = \frac{\text{difference in } y}{\text{difference in } x}$$

$$= \frac{5}{5}$$

$$= 1$$

So the gradient of this line is 1.

Now work out the gradients of the other graphs we have drawn so far.
You should have found that the gradient of the line for all of the graphs is 1.
Now look at the equation of each line and the point where the line cuts through the *y*-axis, what do you notice here?

Look at the equations we have used so far:

$y = x - 1$
$y = x$
$y = x + 1$
$y = x + 2$

and so on.

Now look at where each of their graph lines cuts the y-axis.

$y = x - 1$ cuts at -1
$y = x$ cuts at 0
$y = x + 1$ cuts at $+1$
$y = x + 2$ cuts at $+2$

So this gives us the idea that the last number in an equation, when it is written in this form, tells us where the line will cut the *y*-axis.

What About Gradients?

Use the drop and step method to find the gradient of the line in graph 8.7.

Graph 8.7

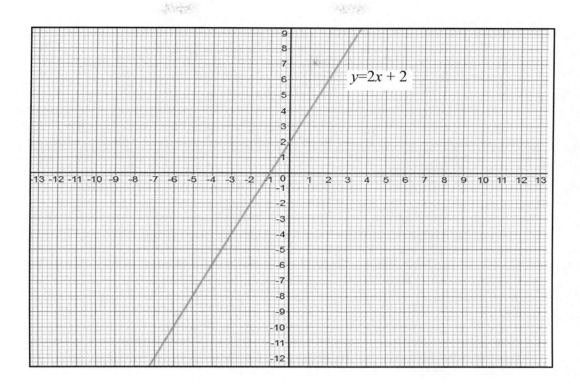

Graph 8.8.

Using the drop over step method, work out the gradient of the line.

And finally graph 8.9.

Graph 8.9

Now compare the gradients you have just calculated. Now compare the value with the coefficients of x in each of the equations. Write down what you notice.

You should have found that the gradients are the same as the coefficient of x in the relevant equation.

The form of the equation is important here, it tells us a great deal. The generalised equation of a straight line graph is written as:

$$y = mx + c$$

where m is the gradient of the line and c is the intercept on the y-axis (the point where the line crosses it).

Remember the coeffcient is the number in front of the x, so it is this number that tells you the gradient of the line.

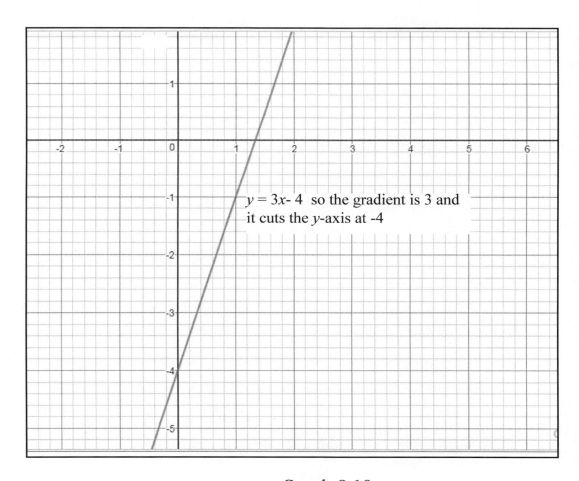

$y = 3x - 4$ so the gradient is 3 and it cuts the y-axis at -4

Graph 8.10

And you can see that this is exactly as we predicted. Notice what we have done here. We have gone from the particular to the general – we have found a general rule that applies to all equations that are written in this form.

This gives a shortcut to imagining what the graph will look like.

Just to make it clear, when we draw the graph of $y = 3x - 4$ we know straight away that it will have a gradient of +3 and will cut through the y-axis at -4.

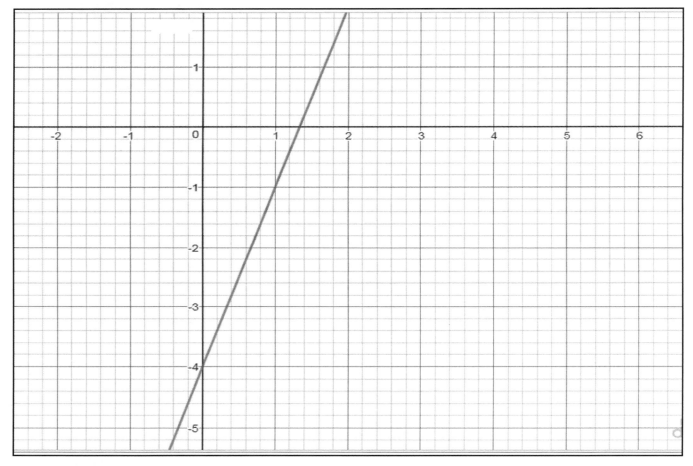

Using this general rule $y = mx + c$ (sometimes written as $y = ax + b$), we can mentally see what the graph will look like. The value of m will tell you exactly what the gradient of the line will be and the value of c will tell you where it will cut the y-axis.

So $y = 6x + 3$ should have a gradient of 6 and cut the y-axis at +3.

Graph 8.11(below) shows what it does look like.

© 2018 Graham Lawler.   Understanding Algebra

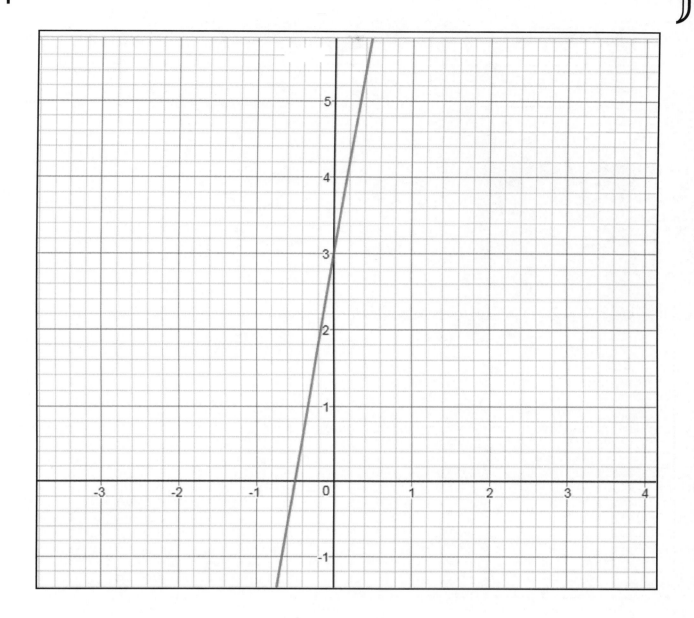

Graph 8.11

Writing equations in different forms

We mentioned above that equations can be written in different forms. Look at this example,

$$x + y = 5$$

This is a simple equation with two unknown variables. We can rearrange the equation to make y the subject by taking x from both sides

$$y = 5 - x$$

This is the form the equation should be in to draw its graph.

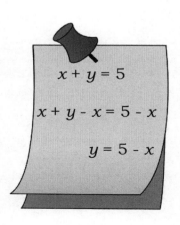

$x + y = 5$

$x + y - x = 5 - x$

$y = 5 - x$

Now let's get a table to give a set of coordinates to plot. We'll do this one step-by-step.

x	-1	0	1	2
y				

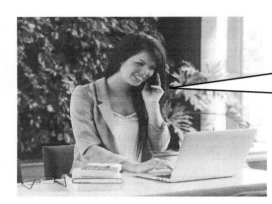

Notice what we have done – we have entered four values of x from −1 to 2.

constant	5	5	5	5
x	-1	0	1	2
y				

Here all we have done is place the equation constant 5 across the columns – this will help in doing the calculations.

Have a go at working out the values and completing the table. Then draw the graph. Do this before having a look at our answer. It will help your understanding.

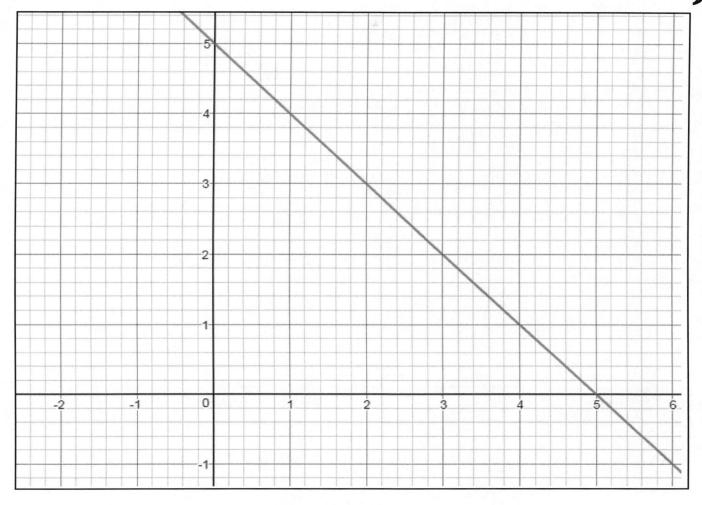

Graph 8.12

Graph 8.12 shows what the graph of $y = 5 - x$ looks like.

Notice the x term is negative in this equation – this indicates that the gradient is also negative.

So we have a set of rules for determining the nature of the graph of an equation:
- the constant (c) gives the intercept on the y-axis;
- if the coefficient of x is negative, the gradient is negative and must slope from top left to bottom right;
- if the coefficient of x is positive, the gradient is positive and must slope from bottom left to top right.

Example 1
Using the equation $y = 6 - 2x$, copy the table below into your journal and complete it.

constant	6	6	6	6	6
x	-1	0	1	2	3
$2x$	-2	0	2		
y		6	4		

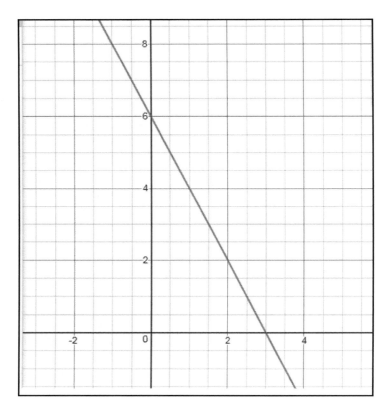

Graph 8.13

Now draw the graph and you should find it looks like that shown in **graph 8.13.**

Exercise 8.1
Draw the graphs of the following equations.

1	$y = x + 4$	**2**	$y = x - 3$
3	$y = x + 7$	**4**	$y = x - 9$
5	$y = 2x + 7$	**6**	$y = 2x + 3$
7	$y = 7x + 7$	**8**	$y = 3x + 2$
9	$y = 8 - 2x$	**10**	$y = 7 - 5x$

Straight Line Graphs and Simultaneous Equations
In Chapter 7 we looked at simultaneous equations and used two methods to solve them – both algebraic. We can also solve them graphically.

Let's look at these two simultaneous equations and their graphs
$$x + y = 7 \quad \text{which rearrange to} \quad y = 7 - x$$
$$2x + y = 10 \quad\quad\quad\quad\quad\quad\quad\quad y = 10 - 2x$$

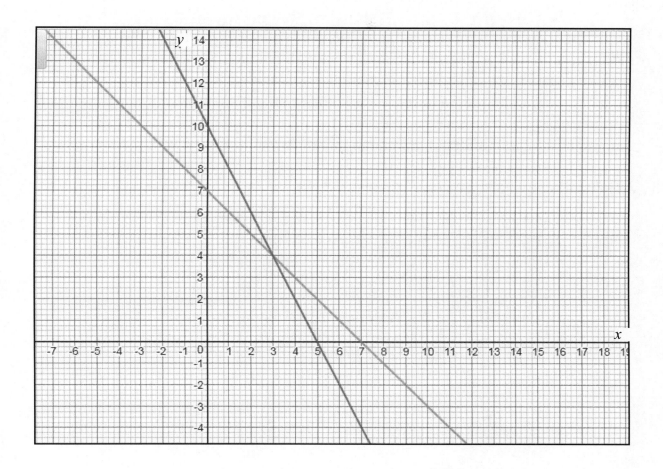

Graph 8.14

The lines in graph 8.14 represent points that satisfy each equation. Because these are simultaneous equations, there has to be a point where the values of x and y are the same on both lines. This point give the solutions to the simultaneous equations.

This must be where the lines cross.

In other words, the point where the lines cross is the only point that satisfies both equations and therefore this must give the solutions.

Here the solutions are $x = 3$, $y = 4$ and this is indicated on the diagram.

Example 1
Find the solutions to these simultaneous equations
Copy and complete the tables below.
First for $y = 9 - 2x$

constant	9	9	9	9	9
x	0	1	2	3	4
$2x$	0	2	4		
y	9	7			

Now for $y = x + 3$

x	0	1	2	3	4
3	3	3	3	3	3
y	3	4			

Now draw the graphs and compare them with ours shown in graph 8.15.

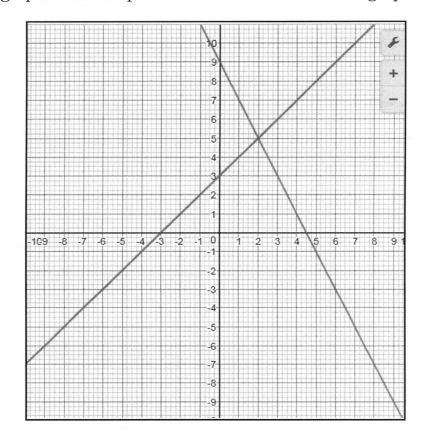

Graph 8.15

Again the values of x and y have been marked on the graph. So $x = 2$, $y = 5$ are the solutions to these equations.

Example 2

Construct the table of values for each equation, first for $y = 10 - 2x$

constant	10	10	10	10	10
x	-2	-1	0	1	2
$2x$	-4	-2	0	2	4
y	14	12	10	8	6

and now for $y = 7 - x$

constant	7	7	7	7	77
x	-3	-1	0	4	6
y	10	8	7	3	1

The graphs look like as shown in graph 8.16 and the solutions are $x = 3$, $y = 4$.

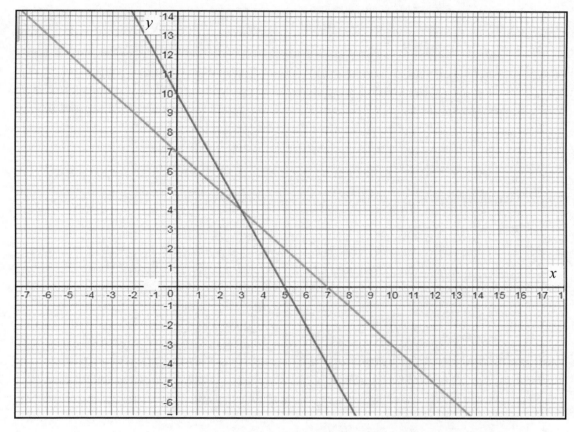

Graph 8.16

Exercise 8.2
Solve the following simultaneous equations by drawing graphs.

1 $y = 8 - x$
      $y = 13 - 2x$

2 $y = 7 - 3x$
      $y = 3 - x$

3 $y = 31 - 3x$
      $y = 24 - 2x$

4 $b = 3 - a$
      $2b = 7 - 3a$

5 $n = 20 - 2m$
      $n = 15 - m$

6 $y = 5 - x$
      $y = 2x + 2$

7 $y = 8 - 2z$
      $y = 6z - 16$

8 $y = 9x + 4$
      $y = 15x - 8$

9 $b = 7 - a$
      $b = 2a - 2$

10 $y = x + 1$
      $y = 10 - x$

Graphing Quadratic Equations

Remember, quadratic expressions are expressions where the highest power of x is 2. So it follows that a quadratic equation is an equation where the highest power is 2.

In this section we are going to look at how to draw quadratic graphs of the form
$$y = ax^2 + bx + c$$

Here is a simple example – graph 8.17 shows the curve for $y = x^2$.

The equation is a curve – in fact it is called a parabola.

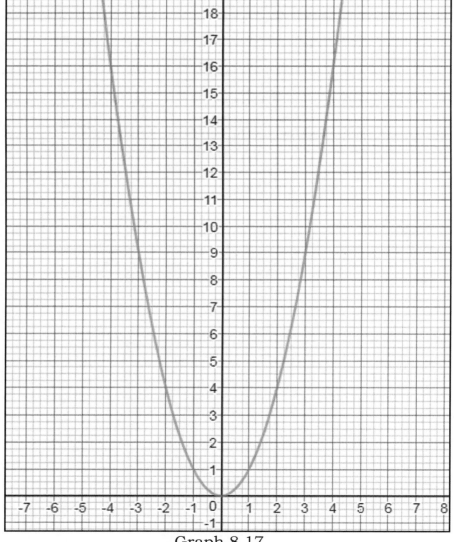

Graph 8.17

Look at what graph 8.17 shows. Every value of y on it is equal to the value of x^2.   So when $y = 1$ we can read across to two points on the curve – at one of these points $x = 1$ and at the other $x = -1$.

Think about this for a moment, it makes a great deal of sense.

Given that the equation is $y = x^2$, when $x = -1$

then $y = (-1) \times (-1)$ which is $= +1$.

When $x = 1$ then $y = (+1) \times (+1)$ which again is $+1$.
So now you can see why quadratic equations have two solutions.

Investigating Quadratic Equation Graphs
Example 1
We will use the equation $y = x^2 + 1$ as a starting point. As usual the first step is to construct a table of values.

constant	1	1	1	1
x	-1	0	1	2
x^2	1	0	1	4
y	2	1	2	5

These (x, y) coordinates are plotted in graph 8.18.

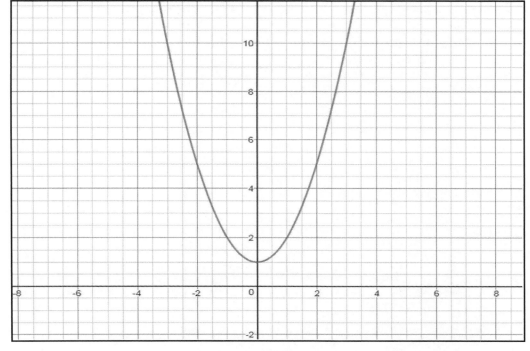

Graph 8.18

Compare this with the graph of $y = x^2$ (graph 8.17). What do you notice?

What do you think the graph for $y = x^2 - 1$ will look like? Make a table of values, draw the graph and compare it with ours shown in graph 8.19.

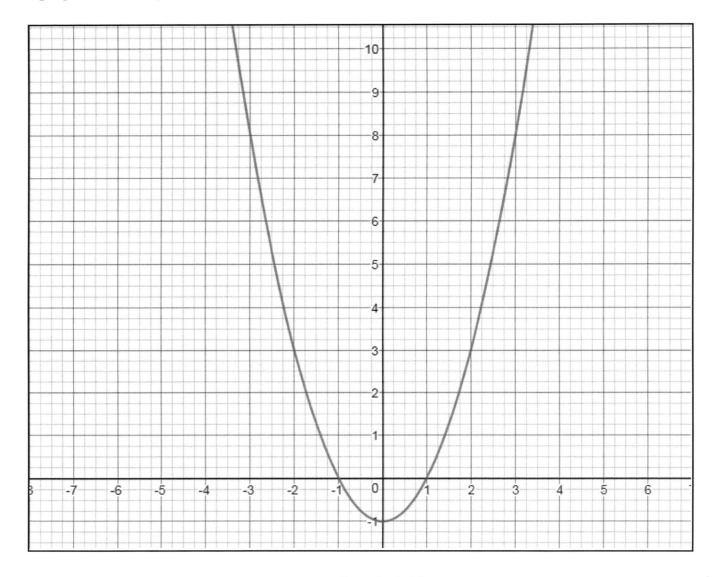

Graph 8.19

What about $y = x^2 - 2$? Maybe you can predict what it looks like now, without constructing a table and actually drawing it?
Have a go at it and then compare your prediction with ours shown in graph 8.20.

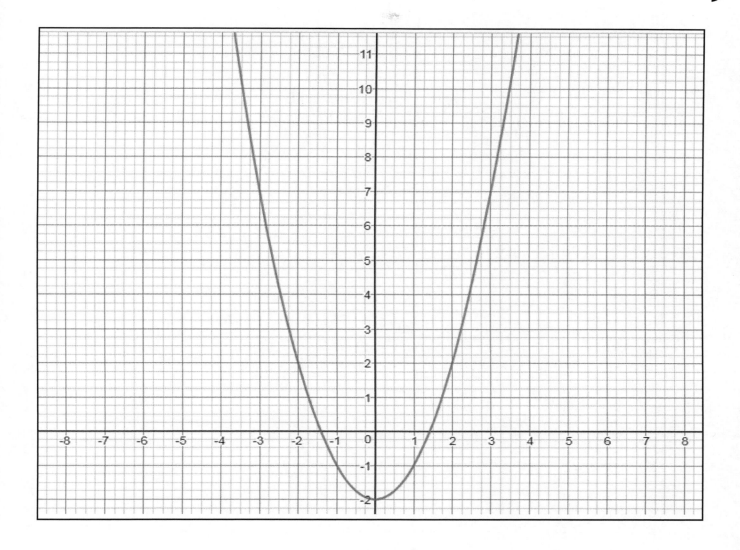

Graph 8.20

In graph 8.21 we have put all these $y = x^2 + b$ curves on the same axes, so that you can see what is happening.

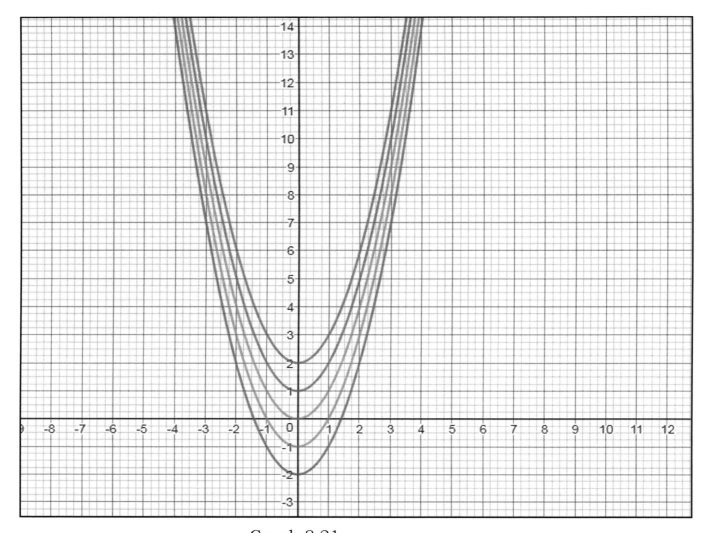

Graph 8.21

You can see that the constant in the equation moves the turning point (the bottom of the curve) up or down the y-axis.

Example 2

What happens if we change the coefficient of x^2?

Draw the graphs of x^2 and $2x^2$ on the same piece of graph paper and look at the similarities and differences in the graphs.

Graph 8.22 shows our version – what do you notice?

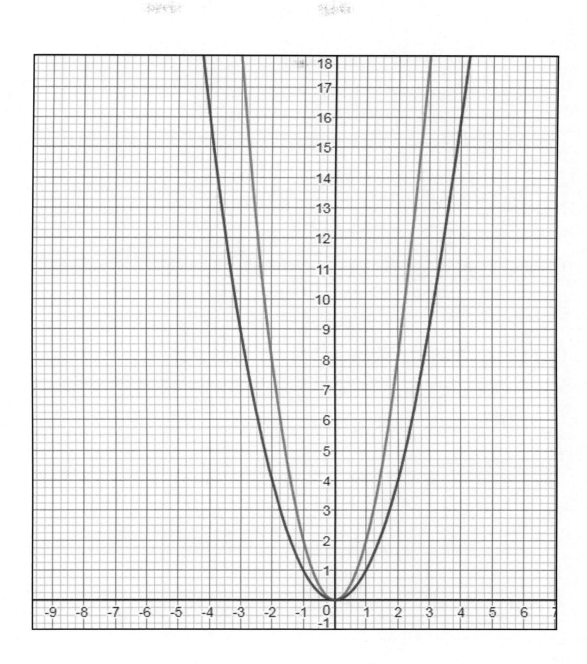

Graph 8.22

Graph 8.23 shows the curves of $y = x^2$ and $y = 5x^2$. As you can see, the larger the coefficient of x^2 then the narrower the curve becomes.

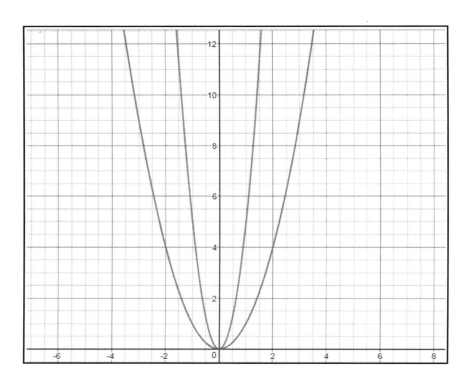

Graph 8.23

Example 3

This is a harder example, $y = x^2 + x$. First, we'll construct a table of values.

x	1	2	3	4
x^2	1	4	9	16
y	2	6	12	20

Now we can draw the graph – it is shown in graph 8.24. Actually we have used more values than given in the table above – this is to show that the graph is symmetrical. You can check it by reading the values of x and y off the graph.

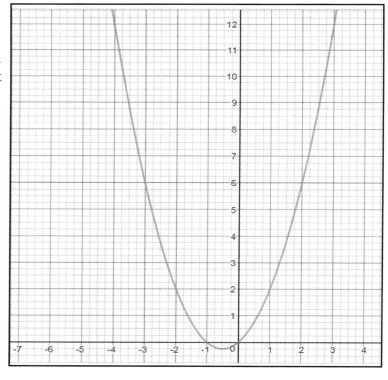

Graph 8.24

Exercise 8.3

Draw the graphs of the following equations using a scale of 2 cm for 1 unit on the x-axis and 1 cm for 1 unit on the y-axis. Use values of x from -10 to $+10$.

1 $y = x^2 + 5x$ **2** $y = x^2 + 7x$

3 $y = x^2 - 4x$ **4** $y = x^2 + 2x + 2$

5 $y = x^2 - 9$ **6** $y = x^2 - 2x + 6$

7 $y = x^2 - 16$ **8** $y = x^2 - 2x - 3$

9 $y = x^2 + 5x - 5$ **10** $y = x^2 + 8x - 7$

What About Quadratics with Negative Coefficients?

Draw the graph of $y = x^2$ and then draw the graph of $y = -x^2$.
What do you notice?   Graph 8.25 shows the curve for $y = x^2$

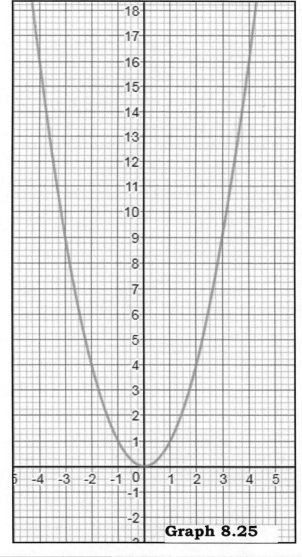

Graph 8.25

Now let's compare it with the graph of $y = -x^2$ shown in graph 8.26. You can see that it is a reflection of the curve for $y = x^2$ in the x-axis.

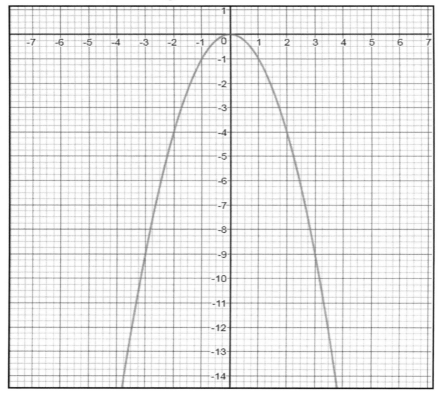

Graph 8.26

So from this we can deduce that when the x^2 term is negative, the curve is inverted.

What About Cubic Curves?

A cubic curve has an x^3 term as the highest power of x. Graph 8.27 is the curve of $y = x^3$

Graph 8.27

 Understanding Algebra

Example 1

Graph 8.28 shows the line for $y = 2x^3$

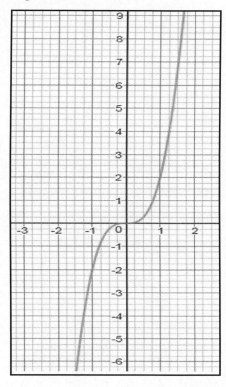

Graph 8.28

Graph 8.29 is the one for $y = 3x^3$

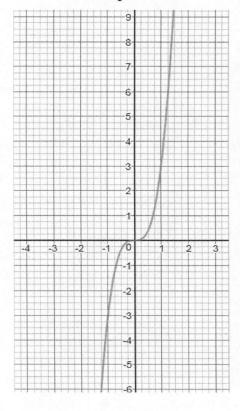

Graph 8.29

When you look at these three graphs individually there is little to separate them – but graph 8.30 shows what happens they are drawn on the same axes.

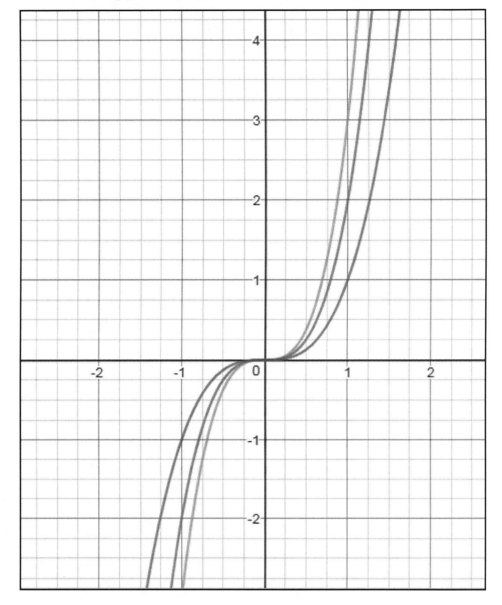

What happens as *x* gets larger? Here is one of those occasions which you really need to investigate for yourself – try different values for the coefficient of *x*.

What happens another term is added? For example,
$x^3 + 3$?

Or
$x^3 + x$? Or $4x^3 + 3x$

Remember – you need to convince yourself first and then convince another person.

You can see that as the coefficient increases, the steepness of the curve also increases.

Example 2

Earlier we suggested that you draw the curve for $4x^3 + 3x$

Graph 8.31 shows what it looks like.

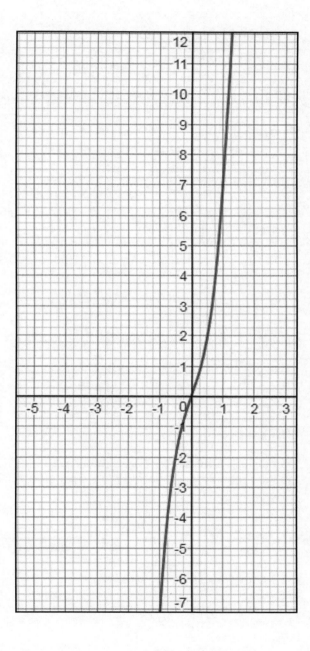

Graph 8.31

Example 3

The other type of cubic curve that you need to be aware of is shown in graph 8.32.
This is the graph of $y = x^3 - 5x + 7$

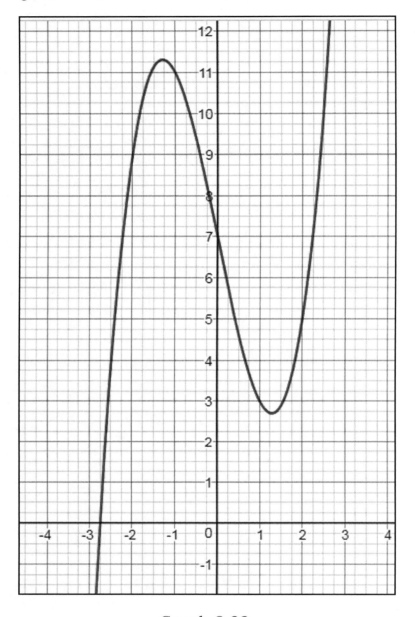

Graph 8.32

You can see in this graph there is a pronounced double turn. This is a common feature of cubic curves.

What Happens When the x^3 Term is Negative?

Investigate this for yourself now. Make a table of values for $y = 8x - 4x^3$
 Use values for x from –4 to +4 and plot the points on a graph. What do you notice about the curve?

Graph 8.33 is for $y = 8x - 4x^3$

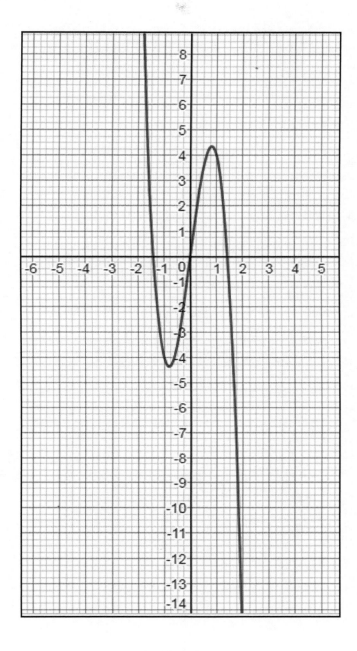

Graph 8.33

You should have worked out that as x gets larger, then so does y but y is negative.

Studymates   © 2018 Graham Lawler.   Understanding Algebra

Reciprocal Curves

The final type of graph that you need to be aware of, in this chapter, is the reciprocal curve. These are derived from equations that include a fraction with an x term in its denominator – for example $y = {}^{11}/_x$

Try a simple case, for example $y = {}^1/_x$.

Draw a sketch in your journal to show what you think this kind of curve looks like.

Example 1

Graph 8.34 shows the curves for $y = {}^{11}/_x$

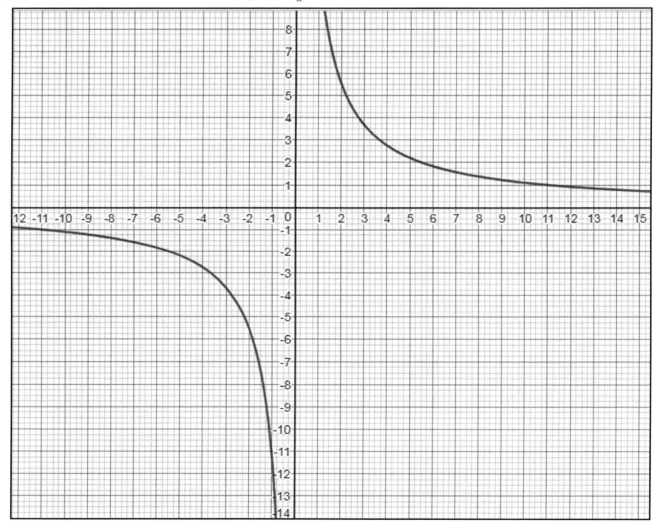

Graph 8.34

Notice that the curve has a break at $x = 0$. The x-axis and the y-axis are called asymptotes to the curve because the curve gets very close to but never actually touches the axes.

Example 2

Let's look more closely how we draw this type of graph using $y = {}^{10}/_x$ as an example.

First build a table of values.

x	-2	-1	0	1	2
${}^{10}/_x$	${}^{10}/_{-2}$	${}^{10}/_{-1}$	${}^{10}/_0$	${}^{10}/_1$	${}^{10}/_2$
y	-5	-10	∞	10	5

The symbol '∞' means 'infinity' – a big number. Also note that you would need more points to draw this graph, but these will give you the idea. It turns out as shown in graph 8.35. Compare yours with this.

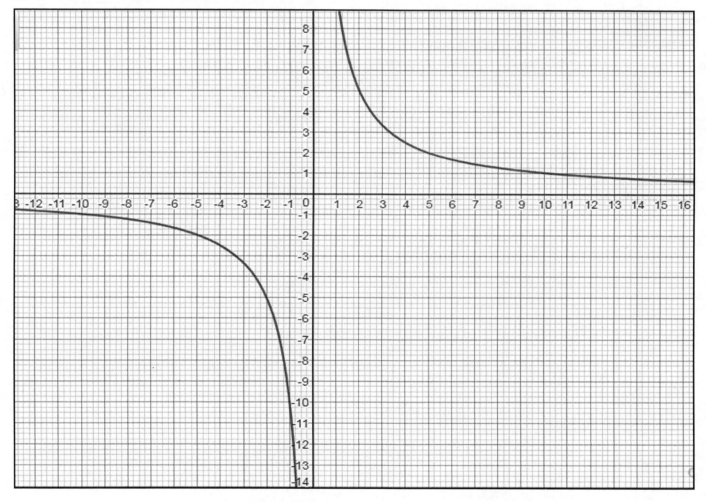

Graph 8.35

Example 3
Try this one on your own, $y = {}^{12}/_x$

Make up a table of values and draw the graph. Graph 8.36 shows ours for you to compare yours against.

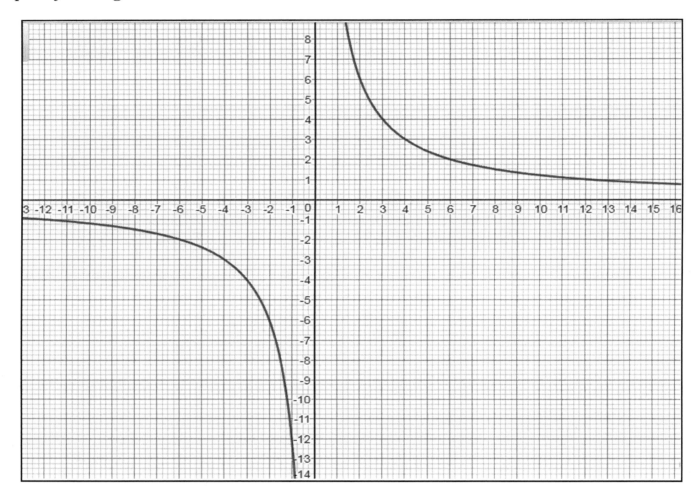

Graph 8.36

Tutorial

Discussion Point
'Drawing graphs of simultaneous equations is easier than using the algebraic methods to solve them.'

Do you think this is true or false? Justify your view to another person. Make a journal entry.

Study Tip
We recommend that you practice drawing the different graphs and use your journal to record the different methods. Try drawing a mind map for each method.

9 Solving Quadratic Equations

One-Minute Overview

Solving quadratic equations is a skill that will be useful throughout your mathematics career. In Chapters 7 and 8 you found that quadratics have two solutions and that this is clearly shown when a graph is drawn

In this chapter you will learn about:
- Factorising (In USA Factoring) to solve equations;
- Using of the formula;
- Using the complete the square method as a way of factorising.

Factorising a quadratic expression means to change its form so that it is in the form $(x + ?)(x + ?)$. When these brackets are multiplied out and all like terms are collected together, we should be back to the expression we started with.

Example 1

Think about the two terms that go where the ? marks are in $(x + ?)(x + ?)$. When these are multiplied together, they need to multiply to +10. This means that they have to be factors of +10. So they must be +5 and +2 or +1 and +10.

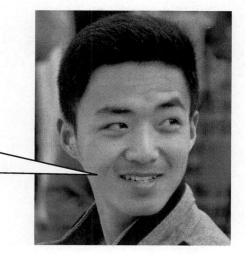

Factorise the expression $x^2 + 7x + 10$

So we need two nunmbers that multiply to but add to the middle term +7 so they muct be +5 and +2

So the final factorisation is $(x + 5)(x + 2)$.

Method 1: Factorising

Think through this yourself before you compare your answer with ours. You need to think in two stages – first of all what numbers multiply to give the constant? and then do they add to give the co-efficient of the middle term?

Example 2

Factorise the expression $x^2 + 3x - 18$

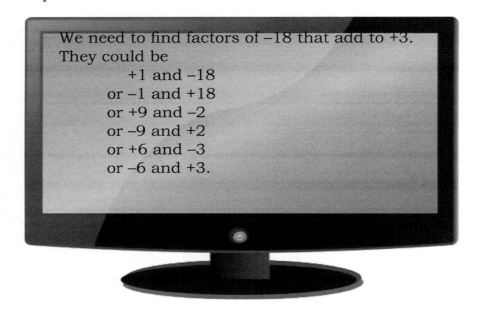

We need to find factors of –18 that add to +3.
They could be

> +1 and –18
> or –1 and +18
> or +9 and –2
> or –9 and +2
> or +6 and –3
> or –6 and +3.

Now, which of these pairs will add to +3?

The only ones are +6 and –3.

So, $x^2 + 3x - 18 = (x + 6)(x - 3)$

So how can we use this technique to solve equations?

You will always find that quadratic equations contain an x^2 term and usually an x term as well as a number term.

Exercise 9.1

Factorise the following quadratic equations.

1     $x^2 + 8x + 12$ 2 $x^2 + 8x + 15$

3     $x^2 + 12x + 20$ 4 $x^2 + 20x + 36$

5     $x^2 + 12x + 35$ 6 $y^2 - 5y + 6$

7     $a^2 - 13a + 12$ 8 $b^2 - b - 20$

9     $x^2 - 2x + 24$ 10 $y^2 - 16$

Think about a multiplication in which two numbers are multiplied to give the answer zero. What does that say about one, or both, of the numbers multiplied? Make a note in your journal.

If you multiply two numbers and get zero then one, or both, of the numbers must be zero. Try some for yourself; 3×0, 5×0, 0×72, 3.2×0, ... It is one of these things that we instinctively know but find difficult to articulate. It is really useful in solving equations.

This is one of those areas in mathematics where you have to use the knowledge you have from another topic in mathematics and apply it in this topic.

Think about what you know happens when you multiply two numbers. Think about the signs of those numbers, what happens if one is postive and one is negative? Both are negative ? Both are positives ?

If you want to get a negative number when you multiply, you need them to be different signs.
If you want a positive answer then the signs must both be the same.

 Understanding Algebra

Let's solve $x^2 + 8x + 12 = 0$ We need to find two numbers that multiply to 12 and also add to 8.
Have a think about this for a moment, what must those numbers be?

Think about the last number in the quadratic, it is +12. Now think about what you know about posiitve numbers.
If you have two numbers that multiply to a positive number, what can you say about those two numbers ?

The two numbers will need to be 6 and 2, so we put them in the brackets as we did earlier.
Now these two brackets are a product – and they multiply together to give zero.
So one or both of them must be equal to zero.

So we can turn the equation
$$x^2 + 8x + 12 = 0$$

into $(x + 6)(x + 2) = 0.$

Therefore either

$x + 6 = 0$ or $x + 2 = 0.$

If $x + 6 = 0$ then $x = -6$.   If $x + 2 = 0$ then $x = -2$.

These are the two solutions to the quadratic equation $x^2 + 8x + 12 = 0$.

Example 2

$$x^2 + 8x + 15 = 0$$

Factorising gives

$$(x + 3)(x + 5) = 0$$

So either $x + 3 = 0$,   or $x + 5 = 0$
and $x = -3$ and $x = -5$.

Exercise 9.2
Solve these Quadratic Equations.

1	$x^2 + 12x + 20 = 0$	**2**	$x^2 + 20x + 36 = 0$
3	$x^2 + 12x + 35 = 0$	**4**	$y^2 - 5y + 6 = 0$
5	$a^2 - 7a + 12 = 0$	**6**	$b^2 - b - 20 = 0$
7	$y^2 - 6y + 9 = 0$	**8**	$a^2 - 4a - 5 = 0$
9	$x^2 - 9x - 10 = 0$	**10**	$b^2 - b - 56 = 0$

What if there is no Constant Term?

$x^2 - 5x = 0$ the left-hand side has two terms with a common factor, namely x.

So we can take this out as a common factor to generate a new equation,

$x(x - 5) = 0$.
We now have a product in which one (or both) factors must be zero.

So either $x = 0$, or $x - 5 = 0$ when $x = +5$.

Exercise 9.3
Solve these Quadratic Equations.

1 $x^2 - 4x = 0$

2 $x^2 + 8x = 0$

3 $2x^2 - 6x = 0$

4 $x^2 - 25 = 0$

5 $6y^2 - 9y = 0$

6 $25x^2 - 1 = 0$

7 $x^2 - 49 = 0$

8 $63x^2 - 21x = 0$

9 $4x^2 = 3x$

10 $y^2 = y$

Mathematics is a 'living' subject this means mathematicians are continually creating or discovering new mathematics.
So we can make use of mathematics developed by previous mathematicians – in other words we do not need to discover everything for ourselves. There is a formula that can be used to solve a quadratic equation.
Here it is and it is well worth memorising.

Method 2: Solution using the Quadratic Formula

The Formula

$$x = \frac{-b +/- \sqrt{b^2 - 4ac}}{2a}$$

Example 1
Solve the equation $2x^2 + 3x - 5 = 0$.

In this case $a = 2$, $b = 3$ and $c = -5$.

So now we simply substitute these values in the quadratic formula.

$$x = \frac{-3 +/- \sqrt{3^2 - 4 \times 2 \times {}^-5}}{2 \times 2}$$

$$x = \frac{-3 +/- \sqrt{49}}{4}$$

$$x = -3 + {}^7/_4 \quad \text{or } -3 - {}^7/_4$$

$$x = {}^{-5}/_4 \qquad \text{or } {}^{-19}/_4$$

$$= -1\,{}^1/_4 \quad \text{or } -4\,{}^3/_4$$

the general form is
$ax^2 + bx + c$

so plug the numbers that these letters represent into the formula.

In most mathematics courses you should use this formula after trying (and failing) to factorise. But if you are asked to factorise in an examination but then use the formula, you will most likely not get the marks – even if you are correct.

Exercise 9.4
Solve these Quadratic Equations using the Formula.

1 $2x^2 + 10x + 4 = 0$ **2** $3x^2 + 11x + 5 = 0$

3 $6x^2 + 12x + 3 = 0$ **4** $3x^2 - 11x + 2 = 0$

5 $5x^2 - 9x + 3 = 0$ **6** $x^2 + 4x + 1 = 0$

7 $3a^2 - 2a - 5 = 0$ **8** $3x^2 - 25x + 9 = 0$

9 $4x^2 - 5x - 4 = 0$ **10** $9x^2 - 6x - 5 = 0$

Method 3: Solution using Completing the Square

Completing the square is a way to solve a quadratic equation if the equation will not factorise.

The general form we want to end up with is

$$y = a(x +/- b)^2 + c$$

Example 1
Look at the equation $x^2 - 8x + 11$, we want to write it in the form

$$y = (x - b)^2 + c$$

To get the b value, halve the coefficient, so the bracket becomes $(x - 4)^2$

Now hang on for a moment, let's look at

$(x - 4)^2$

Can you see a problem with this?

Expand it

$(x - 4)^2 = (x - 4)(x - 4)$

$= x^2 - 4x - 4x + 16$

$= x^2 - 8x + 16$

> Remember we started off with
> $$x^2 - 8x + 11$$
>
> but now we have
> $$x^2 - 8x + 16$$

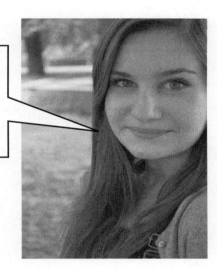

So $x^2 - 8x + 11$ is not the same as $(x - 4)^2$

so we need to take off the square of half the coeffiecient of x

the coefficient of x is -8, half of -8 is -4 and -4^2 is 16

so we need to subtract 16

so $x^2 - 8x + 11 = (x - 4)^2 - 16 + 11$

$= (x - 4)^2 - 5$

> Remember we had +11 but when we have -16+11 the answer is -5

Example 2

To factorise $x^2 + 6x$

it can be seen that $b = 3$ and $c = 9$.

Therefore
$$x^2 + 6x = (x + 3)^2 - 9$$

> Here b is 3 because it is half of 6 and c is 9 because it is 3^2 so we need to subtract 9

Again, prove it to yourself by expanding the brackets on the right-hand side and then adjusting the end number.

Example 3

In $x^2 + 4x + 1$ we use the 'trick' of ignoring the 1 for a while and then putting it back.

So, $x^2 + 4x = (x + 2)^2 - 4$ by completing the square.

Putting the 1 back we get $(x + 2)^2 - 4 + 1$, which simplifies to $(x + 2)^2 - 3$.

As always, prove it to yourself by expanding the bracket.

Example 4

Factorise $x^2 + 12x + 9$

It can be seen that $b = 6$ and $c = 36$.

So the expression we want is $(x + 6)^2 - 36 + 9$, or

$$x^2 + 12x + 9 = (x + 6)^2 - 27$$

Prove this to yourself, then prove it to another person.

Example 5

This is a harder example – well it looks harder to start with, but we can simplify it to make it more straightforward.

Using $4z^2 - 16z + 7$ we need to take out the largest common factor – this is 4, so

$$4z^2 - 16z + 7 = 4[\, z^2 - 4z + {}^7/_4 \,]$$

Now we can rework the right-hand side so that it is in the correct form to complete the square. Have a go at your producing your solution compare it with ours below.

Here is our solution.

$$4z^2 - 16z + 7 = 4[z^2 - 4z + {}^7/_4]$$

$$= 4[(z-2)^2 - 4 + {}^7/_4]$$

$$= 4[(z-2)^2 - {}^9/_4]$$

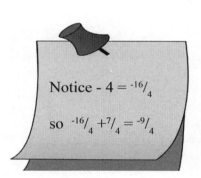

Notice $-4 = {}^{-16}/_4$

so ${}^{-16}/_4 + {}^7/_4 = {}^{-9}/_4$

We can use the completing the square method to solve quadratic equations. Remember Quadratics have two answers.

Example 1

Solve the equation $x^2 - 8x + 6 = 0$ by completing the square.

$$x^2 - 8x + 6 = 0 = (x-4)^2 - 16 + 6$$

$$= (x-4)^2 - 10$$

Think about this for a moment, if

$$x^2 - 8x + 6 = 0 \text{ and}$$

$$x^2 - 8x + 6 = (x - 4)^2 - 10$$

then we can justifiably say that $(x - 4)^2 - 10 = 0$.

Now if we rearrange this equation we get

$$(x - 4)^2 = 10.$$

Therefore, we can take the quare root of both sides

$$x - 4 = +\sqrt{10} \quad \text{or} - \sqrt{10}$$

so by adding 4 to both sides

$$x = \sqrt{10} + 4 \quad \text{or} -\sqrt{10} + 4$$

$$x = 7.16 \text{ or } 0.86 \text{ (2d.p.)}$$

> Here we add 10 to both sides, that 'undoes' the 10 on the left hand side.,

Example 2
Given that $f(x) = x^2 - 6x + 12$, show that $f(x) > 2$ for all values of x

> This looks scary at first but it doesn't need to be – first of all complete the square.

$$x^2 - 6x + 12 = (x\text{-}3)^2 + 12 - 9$$

$$= (x\text{-}3)^2 + 3$$

Try putting in some values into $(x-3)^2 + 3$, say $x = 1$, what happens ?
What about $x = -1$?

Remember $f(x) = (x-3)^2 + 3$

Whatever value of x you put into the bracket, when you square it, it becomes positive and then you add 3. So this will make it bigger than 2. This must mean that $f(x) > 2$

Exercise 9.5

Complete the square for each of these expressions.

1 $x^2 + 6x$ **2** $x^2 - 10x$

3 $x^2 + 2x$ **4** $x^2 + 6x + 1$

5 $x^2 - 6x + 10$ **6** $x^2 + 2x + 3$

7 $x^2 - 6x - 6 = 0$ **8** $x^2 + 2x + 1$

9 $x^2 + x + 1$

10 $x^2 - x - 1$

Tutorial
Progress Questions

Factorise these quadratic equations.

1 $x^2 + 8x + 12 = 0$ **2** $x^2 + 9x + 18 = 0$

3 $x^2 + 14x + 24 = 0$ **4** $x^2 + 19x + 48 = 0$

Use the quadratic formula to solve these equations.

5 $2x^2 + 12x + 4 = 0$ **6** $4x^2 + 11x + 5 = 0$

7 $6x^2 + 9x + 3 = 0$ **8** $5x^2 - 11x + 2 = 0$

9 $x^2 + 6x = 0$ **10** $x^2 - 4x - 2 = 0$

11 $x^2 + 2x = 0$ **12** $x^2 + 6x + 1 = 0$

Discussion Points

•   Write down a sequence of steps for completing the square.
       Explain how to complete the square to another person.

•   Make a journal entry on the work you have covered in this chapter.
       Make the methods clear in your notes. Write an example on the left-hand
       side and put notes on the right-hand side in a different colour. Explain
       the methods to an other person, remember when the other person does
       not understand, your explanation has not been clear.

10 Trial-and-Improvement

One-Minute Overview

We want to introduce you to a useful technique called bisecting an interval. However, to do this we need to take you through an investigation in which we search for the square root of 2. At the end of the investigation we will recap – as always, it is important that you work with us and try the activities as we progress.

In this chapter you will:
- Search for the square root of two;
- Use iteration to solve an equation.

The Search for the Square Root of 2

We are going to concentrate on finding approximate solutions to equations such as

$$x^2 - 2 = 0$$

$$x^2 - 2x - 1 = 0$$

$$4x^2 - 14x + 49 = 0$$

You must not use square root on your calculator – the reasons will become clear as we work through the work, but please bear with us for now.

First of all we are going to look at $x^2 - 2 = 0$.

Rearranging this equation gives $x^2 = 2$.

Rearranging gives us
$x^2 - 2 + 2 = 0 + 2$
so
$x^2 = 2$

This tells us that the solutions of this quadratic equation are the positive and negative roots of 2.

Activity 1

Using your calculator, calculate 1.412, and now 1.422, and then 1.412 – 2, and finally 1.422 – 2.

Look at the calculations you have just done – what does this tell you about ? Explain your deductions to another person. As always, first convince yourself and then convince another person.

It seems logical from, the calculations done above, to deduce that √2 lies somewhere between 1.41 and 1.42.

Remember, we are looking for the solution to $x^2 - 2 = 0$ (or $x^2 = 2$) and clearly √2 is the solution we are looking for but do not use the square root function on your calculator yet.

Let's look at the graph of $y = x^2 - 2$ (graph 10.1) This may help you to understand what is going on.

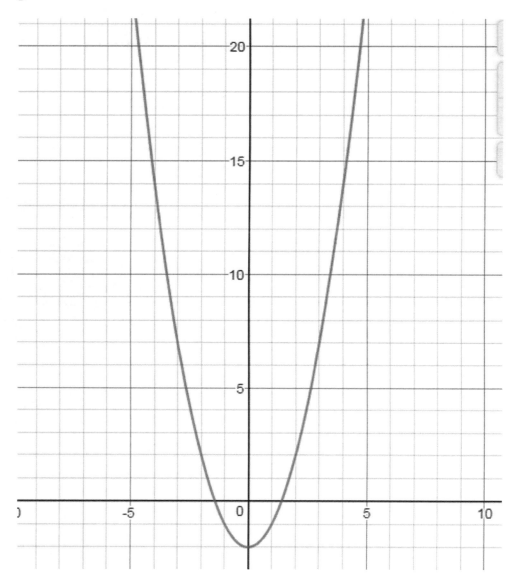

Graph 10.1

You need to be aware that whenever we talk about √2 it is taken that we mean the positive square root – but in this investigation we are interested in both roots as solutions to the equation.

Looking closely at the graph above shows us that the curve lies below the x-axis when $x = 1.41$ or -1.41, and above the axis when $x = 1.42$ or -1.42. Clearly, the graph crosses the x-axis somewhere between these points.

It is at these points where the positive and negative square roots of 2 lie – in other words, when the graph crosses the axis.

So all we have to do is find that spot and we will have found √2. Hmmmm! Let's take a step back.

Activity 2
* How did we determine the values 1.41 and 1.42?
* Calculate $1^2 - 2$.
* Now calculate $2^2 - 2$.

From this we can see that √2 must lie between the consecutive numbers 1 and 2 – simply because $1^2 = 1$ and $2^2 = 4$.

We know that the solution we require lies somewhere between 1 and 2.

We can see from a graph like this that the curve crosses somewhere between $x = 1$ and $x = 2$, but we need to narrow this down.

This means that either that √2 lies between 1 and 1.5, or [1, 1.5], or between 1.5 and 2, or [1.5 ,2].

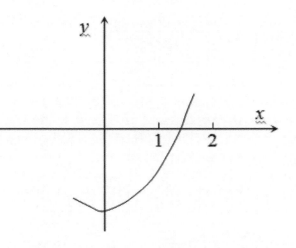

How will we make this determination?
How can we find whether √2 is in [1, 1.5] or [1.5, 2]?

The way to determine in which interval $\sqrt{2}$ lies is to do some simple calculations.

If we calculate 1^2 and then 1.5^2 what will the answers tell us?

We already know that $1^2 = 1$ so if 1.5^2 is greater than 2 we know that $\sqrt{2}$ must lie between these two numbers.

If 1.5^2 is less than 2 then it must mean that $\sqrt{2}$ lies between 1.5 and 2.

Discuss your ideas with another person, remember convince yourself and then convince another person.

Activity 3
Calculate the value of 1.5^2.

Make a journal entry about what this tells you about 1.5^2 .

Now $1.5^2 = 2.25$, so we now know that $\sqrt{2}$ lies between 1 and 1.5

The technique we have been using is called bisecting the interval and with it we can home in closer and closer on the required solution. This is an excellent technique for finding approximate solutions to equations and is commonly known as trial and improvement.

Make sure that you know how we can be certain of this. If the square of the first element in an interval is too small (less than 2 in this example) and the square of the second element is too large (more than 2 in this example) then the solution we are looking for must lie in this interval.

The next step is to bisect the next interval.
Think about what we are doing here – to start with we had a large interval

1 ⟷ 1.5

$\sqrt{2}$

and we had to decide if $\sqrt{2}$ lay between 1 and 1.5 or between 1.5 and 2 – as we have already found, it must lie between 1 and 1.5

So we can draw a new diagram of our interval

$$1 \qquad\qquad\qquad 1.25 \qquad\qquad\qquad 1.5$$

Clearly we need to decide if $\sqrt{2}$ lies between 1 and 1.25 or between 1.25 and 1.5

We already know that the solution cannot be
1 since $1^2 = 1$,

but could the solution be 1.25?

$1.25^2 = 1.5625$.

So this tells us that 1.25 is too small to be the solution.

So this must mean that the solution lies between 1.25 and 1.5.

We can show this in a diagram.

$$1.25 \qquad\qquad 1.375 \qquad\qquad 1.5$$

Now we have to decide if the solution lies between

Again, some simple calculations will show which interval the solution lies in.

1.25 and 1.375, or 1.375 and 1.5.

If we examine the mid-point we can determine whether the solution lies between

> 1.25 and 1.375
>
> or between
>
> 1.375 and 1.5

One run through of a calculation like this is called an iteration.

After one iteration we get the second approximation, after two iterations we get the third approximation and so the process continues. Continuing our example above, $1.375^2 = 1.890625$. This means that   must lie between 1.375 and 1.5.

Again we bisect the interval and select a new smaller interval.

<--->
1.375   1.4375   1.5

When we square 1.375 and if the answer is less than 2, then $\sqrt{2}$ must lie between 1.375 and 1.5, but if the answer is greater than 2 then $\sqrt{2}$ must lie between 1.25 and 1.375. Calculate the value of 1.375^2 and decide which interval $\sqrt{2}$ lies in. Again convince yourself and convince another person.

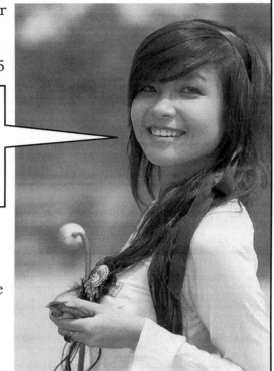

The midpoint in this interval is 1.4375 and again we have to decide if $\sqrt{2}$ lies between

     1.375 and 1.4375 or 1.4375 and 1.5.

So we work out the value of 1.43752 and find that it is 2.06640625.

So because 1.43752 is greater than 2, it must mean that $\sqrt{2}$ lies between 1.375 and 1.4375.
Notice also that we must be pretty close to the value of $\sqrt{2}$ because 2.06640625 is pretty close to 2.

So is $\sqrt{2}$ is going to be very close to 1.4.

Again we need a new interval to bisect,

     1.375   1.40625   1.4375

You know the routine by now – take the midpoint, square it and use this as an indication as to which half of the interval the solution lines in.
     $1.40625^2 = 1.977539063.$

The next interval to examine is [1.40625, 1.4375] but before we do that have a look at the diagram below. By doing this repeatedly we are homing in closer and closer to the value of √2 .

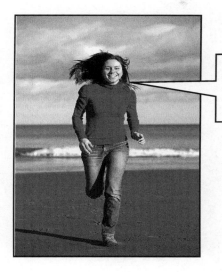

It is like running around a track and getting closer to the centre as you go around

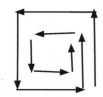

Start

Here is the next interval

1.40625   1.421875   1.4375

Once again work out the square of the midpoint, 1.421875² ≈ 2.021728516

And this is where we are going to leave it because even though we don't have an accurate solution to √2 we have one that is pretty close (2.021728516 ≈ 2).

The truth is that it not possible to determine the value of √2 exactly. We can get closer and closer but iteration will never give an exact determination because √2 is an irrational number.

These numbers fascinated the Greek early mathematicians simply because they could not be determined. This is why we asked you, at the start of this chapter, to avoid using the square root function on your calculator. Electronic calculators are programmed to approximate to √2 somewhere in the region of 1.414213562.

≈ is the symbol we use to say approximately equal

However we have used this investigation as a means of showing you the method of bisecting intervals to find the solution to an equation.

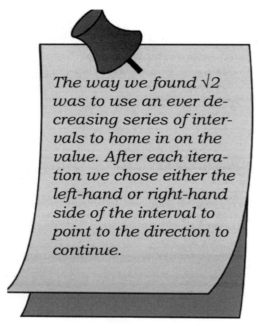

The way we found √2 was to use an ever decreasing series of intervals to home in on the value. After each iteration we chose either the left-hand or right-hand side of the interval to point to the direction to continue.

Tutorial
Progress Questions
Use the bisection method to solve these equations.

1     $x^2 - 18x + 49 = 0$

2     $x^3 + 3x + 3 = 0$

Discussion Point
Explain the bisection of intervals technique to another person. Go through each of the steps logically and make sure they understand why you are doing what you are doing.

Study Tip
We recommend that you use your journal along with a set of mind maps. If you are new to mind mapping read Tony Buzan's excellent book *The Mind Map* (BBC books).

Ex 2.1 p17
1,2,3,4,5,6,7,8,9,10,11,12,13,14,15

Ex 2.2 p20
The next three numbers in the sequence are: 10, 15, 21

The answer to the young woman's first question is 15

Ex 2.3 P25

1	$e = 5s$	**2**	$e = 3s + 1$	**3**	$e = 10s + 1$
4	$e = 2s + 3$	**5**	$e = 3s + 1$	**6**	$e = s^2$
7	$e = 5s + 1$	**8**	$e = 3s$	**9**	$e = 8s + 1$
10	$e = 10s - 1$	**11**	$e = 5s - 1$	**12**	$e = 3s + 5$

Turorial Progress Questions p26

1	1,4,9,16	**2**	**(a)** 10	**(b)** 12	**(c)** 20
3	1,8,27,64	**4**	169		

Ex 3.1 p29

1	-1	**2**	-8	**3**	-8	**4**	1	**5**	2
6	-5	**7**	-7	**8**	13	**9**	-59	**10**	-16

Ex 3.2 p31

1	$4^2 = 16$	**2**	$5^3 = 125$	**3**	$4^3 = 64$	**4**	$9^2 = 81$
5	$7^3 = 343$	**6**	$12^2 = 144$	**7**	$3^4 = 81$	**8**	$13^2 = 169$
9	$14^2 = 196$	**10**	$15^2 = 225$				

Ex 3.3 p33

1	w^3	**2**	m^7	**3**	j^{13}	**4**	a^7	**5**	g^{11}
6	r^2	**7**	e^5	**8**	d^6	**9**	s^{11}	**10**	y^4

Ex 3.4 p34

1	p^6	**2**	j^3	**3**	r^3	**4**	w	**5**	q^6
6	a^3	**7**	m^6	**8**	h	**9**	y^2	**10**	n^6

Tutorial p36 SetA

1	-2	**2**	-10	**3**	-6	**4**	-5	**5**	-2
6	16	**7**	125	**8**	64	**9**	81	**10**	2401

Set B

1	w^4	**2**	m^8	**3**	j^{15}	**4**	a^{10}	**5**	g^9
6	x^{12}	**7**	b^3	**8**	c^2	**9**	y^7	**10**	a^{-2}

Set C

1	p^7	**2**	j^2	**3**	r^4	**4**	w^2	**5**	q^5
6	k^6	**7**	m	**8**	b^{-13}	**9**	n^5	**10**	a^{-10}

Tutorial p46

1   highest power is 1   **2**   highest power is 2   **3**   highest power is 3

4   You subtract each term from the subsequent to get the difference

5   The 1st differences are not the same, then go to the second differences which are a multiple of 2.

Ex 5.1 p49

1	$z = 5$	**2**	$y = 11$	**3**	$v = 7$	**4**	$m = 3$
5	$f = 4$	**6**	$d = 20$	**7**	$a = 12$	**8**	$r = 28$
9	$a = 99$	**10**	$p = 81$				

Ex 5.2 p51

1	$x = 37$	**2**	$v = 27$	**3**	$c = 15$	**4**	$m = 47$	**5**	$k = 55$
6	$a = 20$	**7**	$l = 54$	**8**	$d = 110$	**9**	$q = 190$	**10**	$n = 275$
11	$k = 2$	**12**	$f = -6$	**13**	$k = -9$	**14**	$h = 2$	**15**	$f = -1$

Ex 5.3 p54

1	$y = 6$	**2**	$m = 6$	**3**	$n = 2$	**4**	$y = 3$	**5**	$y = 2$
6	$t = 12$	**7**	$u = 7$	**8**	$r = 1$	**9**	$f = 2$	**10**	$d = 4$

Ex 5.4 p55

1	$x = 27$	**2**	$t = 21$	**3**	$m = 40$	**4**	$y = 48$	**5**	$t = 60$
6	$a = 4$	**7**	$y = 6$	**8**	$p = 33$	**9**	$y = 90$	**10**	$k = 10$

Ex 5.5 p 56

1	$x = 2$	**2**	$x = 2$	**3**	$f = 9$	**4**	$x = 6$	**5**	$r = 7$
6	$t = 1$	**7**	$p = 9$	**8**	$r = 2$	**9**	$y = 8$	**10**	$r = 6$

Ex 5.6 p57

1	$x = 2$	**2**	$x = 9$	**3**	$f = 7$	**4**	$x = 7$	**5**	$r = 6$
6	$t = 1$	**7**	$p = 2$	**8**	$r = 3$	**9**	$y = 10$	**10**	$r = 9$

Ex 5.7 p58

1	$x = 5$	**2**	$y = 2$	**3**	$t = 4$	**4**	$a = 9$	**5**	$y = 7$

Ex 5.8 p59

1	$8c + 48$	**2**	$2a + 6$	**3**	$6t + 30$	**4**	$5u - 40$	**5**	$3r - 27$
6	$6y - 42$	**7**	$4y - 20$	**8**	$6t - 18$	**9**	$35y - 30$	**10**	$49t + 49$

Tutorial p62

1	$k = 3$	**2**	$y = 10$	**3**	$v = 13$	**4**	$m = 4$	**5**	$f = 5$
6	$x = 40$	**7**	$v = 26$	**8**	$c = 17$	**9**	$m = 48$	**10**	$k = 56$
11	$y = 7$	**12**	$m = 5$	**13**	$n = 6$	**14**	$y = 3$	**15**	$y = 2$
16	$x = 27$	**17**	$m = 40$	**18**	$t = 21$	**19**	$y = 48$	**20**	$t = 60$
21	$c = 5$	**22**	$a = 6$	**23**	$t = 2$	**24**	$u = 17$	**25**	$r = 18$

Ex 6.1 p 67

1 $x^2 + 5x + 6$	**2** $x^2 + 6x + 5$	**3** $y^2 + 7y + 12$	**4** $x^2 + 3x - 10$
5 $x^2 + 2x - 15$	**6** $m^2 + 4m - 21$	**7** $v^2 + v - 12$	**8** $z^2 - 15z + 56$
9 $a^2 - 12a + 35$	**10** $d^2 + 13d + 42$		

Ex 6.2 p68

1 $2x^2 - 7x - 4$	**2** $3x^2 + x - 4$	**3** $12d^2 - 25d + 12$
4 $12f^2 - 2f - 30$	**5** $7g^2 - 47g + 30$	**6** $x^2 - 10x + 24$
7 $y^2 - 13y + 42$	**8** $t^2 + 13t + 36$	**9** $168 + 16y - 2y^2$
10 $60y^2 + 3y - 36$		

Ex 6.3 p 69

1      $x^2 + 8x + 16$ 2 $f^2 + 10f + 25$ 3 $x^2 - 6x + 9$ 4 $d^2 + 14d + 49$

5      $m^2 + 4m + 4$ 6 $g^2 - 6g + 9$ 7 $2x^2 - 2x + 5$ 8 $2k^2 + 28k + 100$

9      $2y^2 + 4y + 52$ 10 $10x^2 - 20x + 20$

Ex 6.4 p 69

1      $x^2 + 6x + 9$ 2 $x^2 + 2x + 1$ 3 $x^2 - 10x + 25$ 4 $9x^2 + 12x + 4$

5      $16y^2 + 8y + 1$ 6 $4x^2 + 48x + 144$ 7 $2x^2 + 4x + 2$ 8 $6x^2 + 36x + 54$

9      $5x^2 + 20x + 20$ 10 $5y^2 + 70y + 245$

Ex 6.5 p72

1      $2(4x + 3y)$ 2 $3(3y + 4z)$ 3 $5(2x + y)$ 4 $4(a + 4b)$

5      $5(2x + 3y)$ 6 $9(x - 3y)$ 7 $9(3x - 9y)$ 8 $5(6a - 5b)$

9      $3x(2x - 5)$ 10 $7m(m - 7)$

Ex 6.6 p73

1      $(x + y)(x - y)$ 2 $(t + y)(t - y)$ 3 $(a + b)(a - b)$

4      $(a + 1)(a - 1)$ 5 $(3g + h)(3g - h)$ 6 $(4x + y)(4x - y)$

7      $(x + \frac{1}{2})(x - \frac{1}{2})$ 8 $(3a + 4b)(3a - 4b)$ 9 $(3y + z)(3y - z)$

10      $(4a + \frac{3}{5}b)(4a - \frac{3}{5}b)$

Ex 6.7 p77

1      $(x + 5)(x + 4)$ 2 $(x + 7)(x + 5)$ 3 $(x + 12)(x + 5)$

4      $(x + 7)(x + 3)$ 5 $(x + 15)(x + 1)$ 6 $(x + 5)(x + 3)$

7      $(x + 9)(x + 2)$ 8 $(x + 11)(x + 1)$ 9 $(x + 6)(x + 2)$

10      $(x + 5)(x - +9)$

Ex 6.8 p80

1      $(x - 2)(x + 1)$ 2 $(x + 3)(x - 4)$ 3 $(x + 5)(x - 3)$

4      $(x + 4)(x + 3)$ 5 $(x + 7)(x - 2)$ 6 $(x + 5)(x - 7)$

7      $(x + 9)(x - 2)$ 8 $(x + 4)(x - 4)$ 9 $(x + 12)(x - 1)$

10      $(x + 10)(x - 9)$

Ex 6.9 p90

1 $x = a + b - y$ **2** $x = k + \frac{1}{v}$ **3** $x = hj - b$

4 $x = \dfrac{n(b-v)}{y}$ **5** $x = b - \dfrac{h+d}{n}$ **6** $x = g - \frac{\sqrt{k}}{d}$

7 $x = \frac{y}{f} - a$ **8** $x = \dfrac{ha}{m} - d$ **9** $\frac{1}{9}\left(\frac{y}{d} - a\right)$

10 $x = \dfrac{c - y}{m}$

Ex 6.10 p97

1 **a)** $15n$ **b)** $6n$ **c)** $n + 3$ **d)** $2n + 1$ **e)** $3n - 1$ **f)** $6n - 4$

2 **a)** 12   16 **b)** 100   101 **3** **a)**   19
         30   34 $5n$ $5n + 1$ 20   23
            $3n$ $3n+ 4$ **b)i**   43
                                                            b)ii $4n + 3$

4 **a)** $2n$ **b)** $4n - 3$ **c)**   36 $8n - 4$

5 **a)** $n^2 + 2n$ **b)** $n^2 + 6n$

Tutorial Progress Questions

1 $x^2 + 7x + 10$ **2** $x^2 + 10x + 21$ **3** $y^2 + 6y + 8$

4 $x^2 + x - 20$ **5** $2x^2 - 6x - 8$ **6** $3x^2 - x - 20$

7 $12d^2 - 41d + 35$ **8** $12f^2 - 26f - 16$ **9** $7y^2 - 25y + 12$

10 $x^2 + 14x + 49$ **11** $f^2 + 6f + 9$ **12** $x^2 - 16x + 64$

13 $d^2 + 4d + 4$ **14** $\dfrac{x^2 y^4}{z^4}$ **15** $3b$

Ex 7.1 p105

1 $x = 3, y = 4$ 2 $x = 5, y = 3$ 3 $x = 2, y = 1$

4 $x = 7, y = 10$ 5 $x = 2, y = 1$ 6 $a = 5, b = 10$

7 $a = 9, b = 3$ 8 $a = 1, b = 6$ 9 $x = 4, y = 3$

10 $m = 4, n = 7$

Ex 7.2 p109

1 $a = 7, b = 2$ 2 $a = 2, b = 3$ 3 $m = 6, n = 5$

4 $x = 2, y = 3$ 5 $r = 6, s = 7$ 6 $x = 7, y = 4$

7 $a = 15, b = 5$ 8 $m = 2, n = 7$ 9 $a = 12, b = 13$

10 $x = 1, y = 2$

Ex 7.3 p110

1 8, 4   2 7, 9   3 4,5   4 4,6

5 $w = 25p\ c = 20p$ 6 $a = 70, c = 30$ 7 £20.40   8 $s = £25, c = £80$

9 $i = 50p\ (s = 75p)$ 10 $p = £19.99\ (b = £6.50)$

Tutorial p105

1	$x = 7, y = 2$	**2**	$x = 5, y = 4$	**3**	$x = 3, y = 1$
4	$x = 12, y = 5$	**5**	$x = 2, y = 1$	**6**	7, 2 **7** 15, 12
8	5, 12	**9**	4, 7	**10**	$a = 90p, c = 45p$

Ex 8.1 p120

1

2

3

4

5

6

 Understanding Algebra

7

$y = 7x + 7$

8

$y = 3x + 2$

9

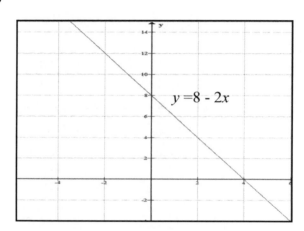

$y = 8 - 2x$

10

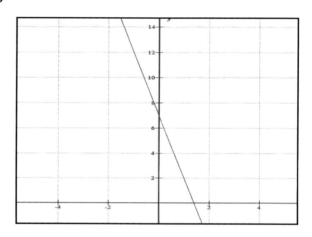

Ex 8.2 p124 The solutions to both equations lie where the graphs cross, because that point is the only point on both lines.

1

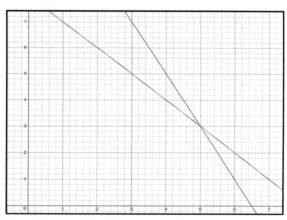

$x = 5, y = 3$

2

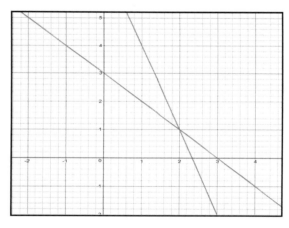

$x = 2, y = 1$

3

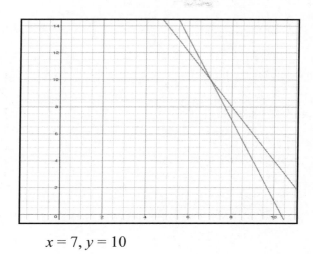

$x = 7, y = 10$

4

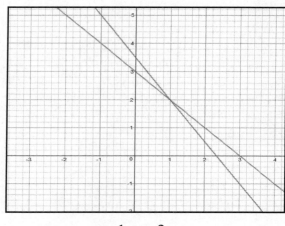

$x = 1, y = 2$

5

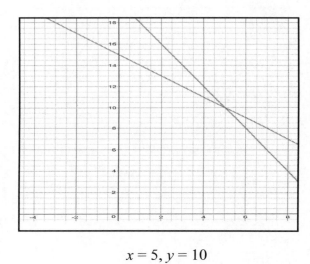

$x = 5, y = 10$

6

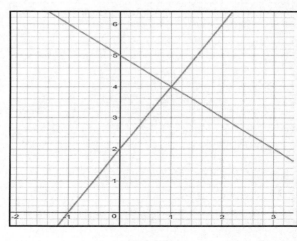

$x = 1, y = 4$

7

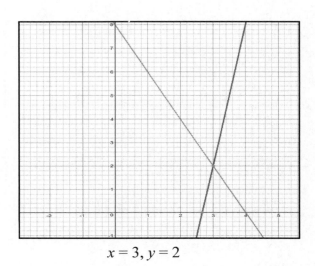

$x = 3, y = 2$

8

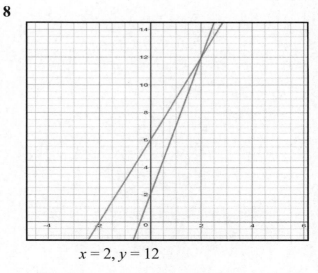

$x = 2, y = 12$

9

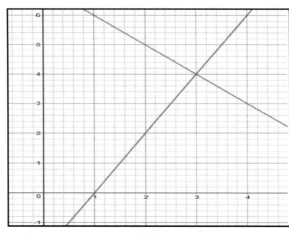

$x = 3, y = 4$

10

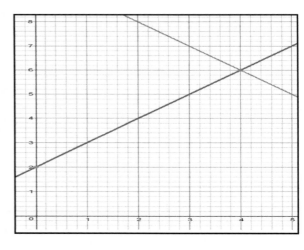

$x = 4, y = 6$

Ex 8.3 p133

1 $y = x^2 + 5x$

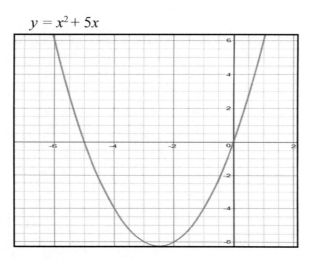

2 $y = x^2 + 7x$

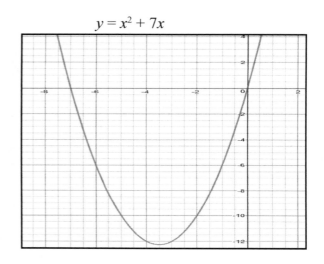

3 $y = x^2 - 4x$

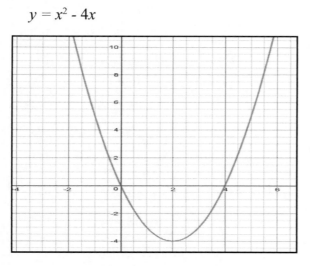

4 $y = x^2 + 2x + 2$

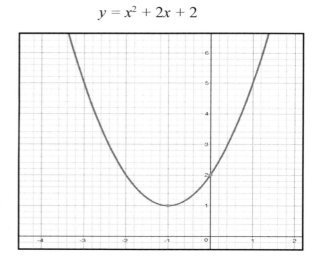

5 $y = x^2 - 9$

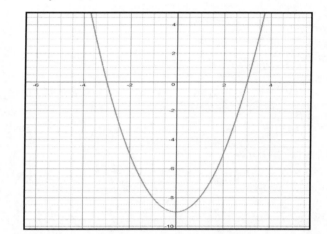

6 $y = x^2 - 2x + 6$

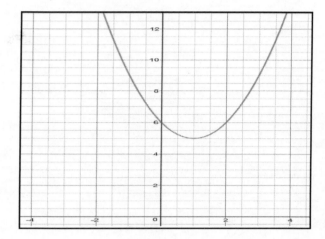

7 $y = x^2 - 16$

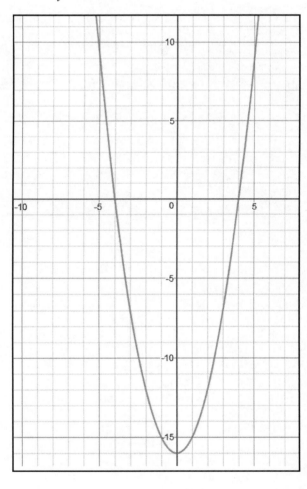

8 $y = x^2 - 2x - 3$

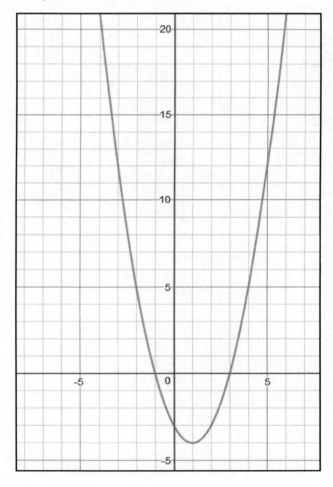

9 $y = x^2 + 5x - 5$

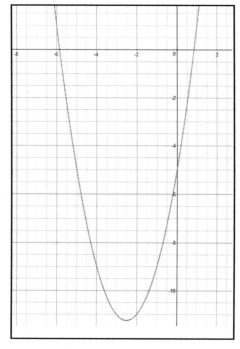

10 $y = x^2 + 8x - 7$

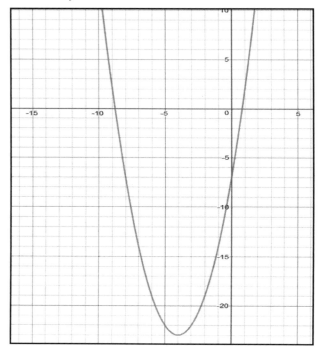

Ex 9.1 p149
1 $(x + 6)(x + 2)$ **2** $(x + 5)(x + 3)$ **3** $(x + 10)(x + 2)$ **4** $(x + 18)(x + 2)$ **5** $(x + 7)(x + 5)$

6 $(x - 3)(x - 2)$ **7** $(a - 12)(a - 1)$ **8** $(b - 5)(b + 4)$ **9** $(x + 4)(x - 6)$ **10** $(y + 4)(y - 4)$

Ex 9.2 p152
1 -10, -2   **2** -2,-18   **3** -7, -5   **4** 2,3   **5** 3,4

6 -4, +5   **7** +3, +3   **8** -1, +5   **9** -1, 10   **10** -7, +8

Ex 9.3 p153
1 4 OR 0   **2** -8 OR 0   **3** 6 OR 0   **4** +/-5   **5** $^3/_2$ OR 0

6 $\sqrt{^1/_{25}}$ **7** +/-7   **8** $^1/_3$ OR 0   **9** $^3/_4$ OR 0   **10** 1 OR 0

Ex9.4 p 154
1 -0.438, -4.56   **2** -0.532, -3.14   **3** 0.207, -1.21   **4** 3.47, 0.192   **5** 1.36, 0.192

6 -0.268, -3.73   **7** $^5/_3$, -1   **8** 7.96, 0.377   **9** 1.804, -0.554   **10** 1.15, -0.483

Ex 9.5 p160
1 $(x + 3)^2 - 9$ **2** $(x + 5)^2 - 25$ **3** $(x + 1)^2 - 1$ **4** $(x + 3)^2 - 8$ **5** $(x - 3)^2 - 1$

6 $(x+1)^2 + 2$ **7** $(x+3)^2 - 15$ **8** $(x+1)^2 - 2$ **9** $(x + ^1/_2)^2 - ^5/_4$ **10** $(x + ^1/_2)^2 - ^5/_4$

Tutorial p158

1 $(x + 2)(x + 6)$ **2** $(x + 3)(x + 6)$ **3** $(x + 2)(x + 12)$ **4** $(x + 3)(x + 16)$

5 -5.646, -0.354   **6** -2.175, -0.575   **7** -1, -0.5,   **8** 2, 0.2   **9** -6,0

10 -0.449, 4.449   **11** 0,-2   **12** -0.172, -5.828

Tutorial p168

1 14.66 or 3.34   **2**   -2.1

Index_A

Also from Studymates

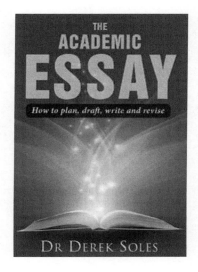

The Academic Essay :
How to Plan, Draft, Write and Revise
Paperback Studymates in Focus S. English
 Dr. Derek Soles ,
Edited by Edward G. James
9781842854259 Paperback 160 pages
All students have to write essays and writing the
essay itself is a learning experience yet many are
never taught how to compose an essay. The act of
writing the essay is a learning experience in itself;
it develop's the student's thinking ability and helps
them to form a coherent and logical argument.
This is why the construction of the essay is important and why it needs to be taught and why it is
surprising that so many students are not actively
taught this skill. This title solves that problem.

Perfect Grammar:
How to Recognise, Correct and Avoid
Grammatical Errors
 Dr. Derek Soles
978-1842851364   Paperback: 178 pages
Who else wants to make their writing sparkle?
How often have you written something and not
been sure if it is correct? Should you write 'its'
'it's' or 'it is'? Armed with this book, you will
never make those errors again. This is an essential guide for students and teachers in post-16
education and for people in business. Communication is essential in any organisation and good
grammar is the 'oil' that lubricates the flow of
communication.

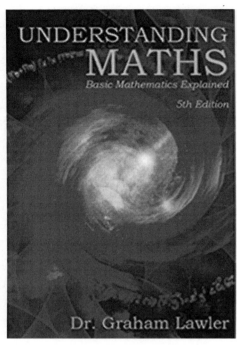

Understanding Maths
Dr Graham Lawler
Paperback: 160 pages
Publisher: Studymates; 5 edition
Language: English
Who else wants to spend less time studying and be able to calculate correctly each time?
This book is aimed at anyone - adults and children alike - who is having trouble with basic mathematics
This book includes details on: * Numbers and place value, * Dealing with fractions, * Calculating with percentages, * Working with decimals, * Using a calculator, * Angles and turning, * Area and volume, * Data handling, * Probabilities and chance, * Estimating and checking

Ideal for Functional skills/ Core Skills/ ESW

5.0 out of 5 stars Excellent book
I have not looked at maths since I left school over 15 years ago, back then I did not understand it. This book has helped be get to grips with learning maths again and developing a proper understanding of how it is done.

5.0 out of 5 stars Fantastic book!
After leaving school nearly 20 years ago and now requiring a maths gcse I was anxious about learning again. However this book helped me move from an E grade to a B grade in a few short months. The book is easy to follow, understand and makes maths enjoyable. This book is highly recommended to anyone looking to enter into the world of maths.

5 out of 5 stars The best book I've ever bought.
I am restarting education at 41 years old, hoping to increase my employment chances if the recession bites.
I believe that mathematics is an essential skill, but I lack confidence, probably because of bad experience as as child. This book changes that. It is written in such a clear, straightforward way that I'm wondering what my problem was with this subject; dare I say it, mathematics appears to be enjoyable. The beauty of it is, all my questions are answered in a way that makes the subject interesting...'

 Understanding Algebra